"Nothing scares you— not these days."

Tim shook his head. "When I married you, you were the most beautiful rabbit in the county."

She stared at his face, memorizing his features. *What should I say,* she thought. *That I've grown up. That I've learned about the hard world.* In the end, she told him nothing.

"You have changed," he repeated. "Very much."

"Of course, I have." Terry stabbed at him. "How could I help it. What do they say? 'Love dies when beauty flies out the window.' Or something like that. It's all gone now."

"Don't kid yourself," he returned harshly. "Sure, all that ethereal virginal beauty is gone, but that was all kid stuff. Now you've become a real woman, Teresa Maria—a real woman. And the rabbit seems to have turned into a tiger."

Emma Goldrick describes herself as a grandmother first and an author second. She was born and raised in Puerto Rico, where she met her husband, a career military man from Massachusetts. His postings took them all over the world, which often led to mishaps—such as the Christmas they arrived in Germany before their furniture. Emma uses the places she's been as backgrounds for her books, but just in case she runs short of settings, this prolific author and her husband are always making new travel plans.

ICE LADY
Emma Goldrick

Harlequin Books

TORONTO • NEW YORK • LONDON
AMSTERDAM • PARIS • SYDNEY • HAMBURG
STOCKHOLM • ATHENS • TOKYO • MILAN

Original hardcover edition published in 1985
by Mills & Boon Limited

ISBN 0-373-17093-9

Harlequin Romance first edition September 1991

ICE LADY

Printed in U.S.A.

CHAPTER ONE

THEY FLEW PAST Mount Dundas below the level of its great flat top, with the wheels already down, and the sunlit runway before them gleaming like a black serpent among its huge snow fields. The 707 had seen better days before it joined up with MAC—the Military Airlift Command—and was pitching in the crosswind as they groped down towards Thule's only runway. Within its warm cocoon it carried five crewmen, one hundred and sixty-seven replacement airmen—and one woman.

Lieutenant Teresa Alden huddled herself up in the jump seat behind the pilot and watched in fascination as the massive Greenland ice-cap rushed up at them. For the first time in six years she felt almost free of the furtive need to huddle in corners, to keep looking over her shoulder, to be prepared to break and run at the smallest suggestion that he might have found her. But how much of her feeling was new-found security, or how much was the deadening of her spirit after all those years of fear, she could not tell.

The sound that broke her reverie was the tyres kissing the concrete. The plane bounced, then settled back again as all four sets of wheels found solid ground. The craft waddled down the runway like a tired duck, and turned off on the taxi-way.

The co-pilot reached over his shoulder for the public-address microphone and grinned at her. 'This is your Captain speaking,' he announced. 'Welcome to the top of the world. The local time is 2100 hours, April tenth. The sun will set at 2300 hours, and will rise again at 0100 hours. The local temperature is eighteen degrees below zero, Fahrenheit. Thank you for flying MAC. Have a good tour.'

He laughed at her as he hung up the microphone. 'Keeps the passengers happy,' he said. 'We'll take your patient off first, nurse. Lucky you were on board when the poor kid went sick. There's the ambulance coming up now. You think it's appendicitis?'

'Nurses don't diagnose,' she told him in her surprisingly deep contralto, 'but if you were a betting crew—'

'Which we are,' he laughed again. He rubbed sleep specks from his eyes. It had been a long flight from central New Jersey. The aircraft wheezed asthmatically to a stop, and an ambulance appeared on the taxi-way by the forward door.

'Well, thanks for the front-seat view,' she told the pilot. She unbuckled her seat-belt and stretched up to her full five feet two inches. Then Teresa swung her bag on to her shoulder and walked out into the main cabin.

The process of manoeuvring the stretcher-basket down the stairs took priority over all other unloading. The tiny windows of the plane were crowded with watchers, impatient to debark themselves. When the sick airman was finally off-loaded, Teresa followed.

Two orderlies manoeuvred the stretcher into the back of the ambulance while Teresa stood just behind them, her eyes making a full circle as she waited. White on white, she told herself. Good God, what a place. Nothing green. No sign of tree or bush. And not a bird or insect sound to be heard.

The settlement lay below the far end of the runway. Rows of identical buildings, raised on pilings above the arctic permafrost, and all painted grey. They looked like gigantic freezer compartments, with tiny windows showing specks of light. The snow was piled plough-high on each side of the street that separated the buildings, with rope-guides strung between each of the buildings. The sun was sinking rapidly in the south-west, casting the shadow of the southern mountain completely over the base, and glittering from the metalwork of the few structures that topped the northern mountain. Grey on white on white! She took a deep breath, and felt the shock as the super-cooled air hit her lungs.

A tall thin woman, almost completely covered by a multi-layered parka, came around from the front of the ambulance, 'Ellen Shannon,' she introduced herself. 'Do we call you Teresa?'

'Most people call me Terry,' the girl replied hesitantly. Another new face. Another group to meet, to work with, but not to mingle with! Six years of running!

The first year had been the hardest. She had spent most of it in the hospital as a succession of surgeons, using the most modern micro-surgical techniques, had laboured to save her hand. And papa and the family were close at hand. And then the quick move to Boston, and two years of nurses' training at Massachusetts General. How quickly it had all passed. All the girls—whose names escaped her now. All the excitement. All the worry. And on the day she had sat for her examinations, she had come back to her little apartment completely worn out. Her landlady had congratulated her, and then, 'Oh yes. There was a man here early today looking for a Teresa Cabral. Does the name mean anything to you?'

'Teresa Cabral?' Her heart had jumped into her throat, and her pulse raced, 'What did he want? What did you tell him?'

'What could I tell him? I don't know any Cabral. I told him we had a Teresa Alden, but no Cabral. He went off in a hurry.'

'I—thank you,' she had said. And had gone up to pack her bags immediately. Early the next morning she had phoned for a cab, and had left the house before seven o'clock, bound for the airport. As the cab pulled away from the house a blue Ford had driven up. Peering out of the rear window of the cab, she saw a tall husky shape climb out of the car, and she knew that she had escaped just in time.

And then the hunt had begun. She fled to Chicago with her new nursing license, and huddled in the centre of the city, looking for anonymity. For six months she found it, but then the hospital published its revised Nursing Register, and within a month the men came, asking questions. She hadn't stopped to say goodbye, she just ran. And after that it became harder and harder. She *had* to use her right name, or forfeit her licence—and without the licence she could not work.

The more she ran, the fewer references she had dared to produce, until even finding jobs became difficult. She dared not make friends, nor mingle with her fellow workers. From Chicago to Cincinnati to Denver, and then to the smaller towns. Huntsville, Alabama; Ardmore, Oklahoma; San Pedro, California. And when the faceless questioners came up on her in Presque Isle, Maine, she had jumped to the safety of the Air Force, leaving behind her a scattered trail of people who might, some day, say 'Alden? Wasn't she the quiet one who always looked scared to death?' Or perhaps they would not even remember *that* much!

A hand touched her shoulder and shook it gently. She turned away from her memories, and smiled that placid smile which had become her mask. 'Shannon—you remember?' the other girl was saying. 'You look as if you've already started back to the lower fifty.'

'I—I'm sorry,' she mumbled. 'I was thinking.'

'Don't worry about it. You didn't get any sleep on the plane, I suppose? Load up over here. We get to ride in the front of the ambulance.'

'That's a big deal?' Terry queried.

'Happens to be the only vehicle in our detachment that has a working heater in it. Forget your luggage. That's one of the few perks you get for being a woman in this crazy place. Somebody will bring it over sooner or later.'

Terry stuck her head into the rear of the ambulance to say a word to her young patient, then climbed into the high front seat between Ellen and the driver.

'Dr Fine didn't come out to the flightline?' Terry asked. 'He's the one I talked to by radio when the airman collapsed.'

'Nope. He's the Medical Chief. He's at the Officers' Club. There's some sort of social meeting with the Base Commander and all the wheels.'

'So who is the doctor in the back of the ambulance?'

'That's Himself. Captain Callagher. He's the chief surgeon. By the way, Dr Fine was pleased with the way you handled that little airborne emergency.'

'I really didn't do anything. I just made him comfortable, and put an ice-pack on him. I didn't expect the place to be so big. We have a chief of medicine as well as a chief of surgery? How many doctors are there?'

'That's it, babe. Just two. We substitute titles for monetary reward around here. It gives them both a better feeling.'

The ambulance jerked forward, tyres squeaking across the dry powdered snow. They made a wide swing around the back of the hangar line, plunged down a steep incline to the level of the buildings, and slowly crunched their way along one of the narrow streets. Ahead of her, six blocks away, Terry could barely discern the place where the snow-covered earth gave way to snow-covered sea. A round dozen huge oil-storage tanks, painted grey and white, clustered near the shore. A long narrow finger of a pier stuck out into the bay.

'Don't have much to say?' Ellen's comment started Terry back to attention.

'I—no,' she stammered, and left it there. How do you politely tell people that you don't want to mix with them. How do you explain that you are a hermit in the middle of society, bound and chained to your ghosts by fear?

The ambulance squeaked up a ramp in front of the last building in the row. A small Red Cross sign was the only thing to distinguish it from all the other buildings. That, and a number stencilled on the corner. The two orderlies bounced out of the rear of the vehicle and whisked their patient into the building. The doctor followed wearily. She could tell by his stride, by the way his shoulders drooped, that he was a tired man. Ellen was tired too. The lines of fatigue ran across her mobile face, and her eyelids were dangerously close to closing.

Terry followed the other girl out of the truck, stretching desperately to find a toe-hold in the snow. As Ellen stomped up the wide stairs, Terry took another look around. Ultima Thule, she thought—the end of the world! And then, unbidden, the stern contorted face of her mother-in-law flashed into her mind.

'You can run,' she had said in that last terrible meeting in the hospital. 'Run all you want to. He'll find you. He'll follow you to the end of the world!' And if you run to the end of the world, and he finds you? Do you—jump off? Terry shuddered, but not from the cold.

'Hey, don't day-dream on the front steps!' Ellen had come back to place a hand on Terry's shoulder, and was urging her towards the entrance to the building. They went through a double compartment of doors, designed in order to create a large airlock. 'Leave all your outer gear here in the hall,' Ellen told her. 'No outside clothing goes into the main hospital. We'll get you properly equipped from Stores as soon as possible. Did you bring plenty of white with you? That's what we normally wear, except for formal doing at the Club.'

'I—yes. I brought everything. I should leave my coat out here?'

'Yes. Arctic survival practice,' Ellen replied as she hung her parka up on a numbered hook. 'It's not critical right now, but in the depths of winter, or in a bad storm, it's important. This side of the door is unheated. If you take your outdoor clothes inside you'll get water vapour in the linings. Then when you go back out, that vapour will instantly freeze. It's especially important for face-masks. Don't forget. One little mistake up here kills you.'

Terry nodded, understanding, as she followed Ellen through the hospital's two open wards, and into the nurses' quarters just beyond. The corridor narrowed when they passed through the swinging doors at that end. Now it was a tiny alley flanked on either side by closed doors. Ellen knocked twice on the first door, and without waiting for an answer pushed into the room. A middle-aged woman in white was sitting at the desk. She looked over her shoulder at them, then got up slowly to greet Terry.

'Major Malson,' she introduced herself. 'You'll call me Mary on nice days, and ma'am when I'm mad. You're Teresa Alden? Sit on the bed there. Make yourself at home.' She brushed half a dozen books on to the floor to make room.

'She prefers to be called Terry,' Ellen interjected.

'Terry?' The elderly nurse ran her eyes over the tiny figure in front of her, noting the raven curls close-cut around her head, the slightly olive complexion of her skin, the outstanding figure half hidden by her crumpled blue uniform. 'My, but you're a well-developed pint of peanuts, girl.'

Terry smiled nervously at her, not sure how to take this slim white-haired woman. 'It comes from my Portuguese blood,' she said hesitantly.

'Portuguese blood? Alden? That's Plymouth Rock, John and Priscilla, Myles Standish, the Mayflower.'

'I married into the family,' Terry stuttered. She blushed and lowered her eyes. The other two watched her, expecting more. What do you want from me, Terry screamed inside her skull. Shall I tell you it didn't work? Shall I tell you I ran away from him, frightened for my life? Shall I tell you how he divorced me while I was still in the hospital? Shall I tell you how his mother hated me? Hated me! And in the end, as usual, she told them nothing.

'Ahh,' the major responded by clearing her throat. 'Well, all we require around here is that you be able to push pills and take temperatures. As long as you can do that we'll get along okay. Take a look around this room, by the way. All our rooms are the same size. You get the next one down. One bed, small size. One armchair. One dining chair, one small table, one bookcase, one wardrobe. You're entitled to decorate as you wish, and as a special dispensation, the Base Commander allows us to choose our own window curtains. How about that?'

'At my last civilian hospital I had a room about five feet smaller, and only one chair,' Terry said softly. 'This looks like the lap of luxury.'

'Don't forget the curtains,' Mary said. 'Very important. Get some, and keep them closed.'

'I—I don't understand,' Terry murmured.

'Ellen,' the chief nurse asked, 'how about scooting down to the pantry and getting us some coffee?' Ellen nodded and disappeared down the hall.

'We have our own little kitchen and showers down there,' Mary told her. 'Before you've been here too long you'll begin to acquire the siege mentality, like the rest of us. I might as well lay it on the line for you. Every airman, from basic ranks to senior officer, is here for twelve months. There are about seven hundred of them in the permanent party. More when units fly in for manoeuvres. After their first two months here, no matter how nice they are, they all start to get itchy. There are three of us women here. Three women, and seven hundred men. It's some sort of powder keg.

'At home, every one of these guys is a fine fellow. But we're not at home. There are only two ways to play it. If you like men, find yourself a big strong husky one, and stick to him like a leech. If you don't care for the strong, protective type, keep your hands and eyes off every man on the Base.

No cuddling in corners, no stray kisses, no lingering hand-holding. If you take one man and stick to him, the rest will leave you alone. But if you try to play the field, all seven hundred of them are going to think you're for free, and they'll line up to get their share.'

'Coffee?' Ellen interrupted. She passed around the steaming liquid in heavy enamelled mugs. 'Is this the basic sex lecture?'

'I—you needn't worry about me,' Terry stammered. 'I'm not available.'

'With a figure like yours,' Ellen scoffed, 'there'll be plenty of them willing to try to make you available.'

'That's enough,' Mary commanded quietly. Her sharp eye had seen the flash of fear, of withdrawal, which changed the girl's face from its placid composure to a haunting, troubled awareness. 'What are your qualifications, Terry?'

'I—paediatrics, mainly. I guess there's not much call for that up here?'

'Don't be too sure,' Ellen laughed. 'In the summer the Eskimo families from Etah occasionally come down. If the Liaison Officer gets government approval, we process them through a complete physical. Men, women, and children.'

'Inuit,' Mary commented. 'Not Eskimo—Inuit. Eskimo is the name that the Athabascan Indians gave them. They call themselves Inuit. Or Greenlanders. There aren't too many pure-blooded Inuit left any more. And what else can you do, Terry?'

'Well, I've done two years in surgical ORR techniques. And then I was cross-trained as a flight nurse in the C-9 Nightingale programme.'

'Now if you can fill teeth on the side, we've got it made,' Mary laughed. 'Our only dentist has gone out to Camp Century for three weeks.'

A heavy fist banged on the door. 'Is there a nurse on the premises?' The masculine voice was sharp and deep.

'Come on in, Jim,' Mary called. 'Everyone here is decent—well, I mean everyone here is dressed.'

'That's too bad.' A man about thirty pushed open the door and walked in. He was of whippet construction, lean, supple, and just a shade under six feet. 'Ah, the wandering Lieutenant Alden?' Terry nodded acknowledgement.

'Dr Jim Callagher, surgeon.' Mary completed the introduction. 'Anything yet on the boy?'

'No. They haven't finished the blood work yet, but I'd be ninety per cent sure it's his appendix. I'll have to have everyone help on this one. Julius will have to do the anaesthetic. I wish the hell we had a surgical nurse. You're a good kid, Mary—'

'Major, if you please.'

'You're a good kid, Major, but you're beat to death, and you shouldn't have to fill in at everything in the world, you know.'

'I thank you for those kind words,' Mary laughed, 'but your problem is solved. Teresa is a surgical nurse.'

'Well now, is it true, acushla?' the surgeon asked.

'Oh, come off the blarney,' Ellen said. 'We all know you were born and brought up in Boston.'

'South Boston,' he returned. 'There's a difference.'

'Yes it is,' Terry interjected.

'What did you say?' All three of them turned to her.

'I—I just said yes. It's true. I'm a qualified surgical nurse. But I didn't really sleep on the plane, and I'm bushed. Perhaps I could sneak in ten winks? A little nap always improves my terrible disposition.'

'I wish I could arrange it,' Jim said. 'But there's a complication. Julius—Dr Fine—is over at the Officers' Club. They're having a little welcome do for a couple of visiting scientists—the pair of them are due to go on to Camp Century in about forty-five minutes. Julius has been talking to the Base Commander about you, and Colonel Hibbs wants you to come over there for a few minutes. So now, if you'll spring up and do this little errand, then both Julius and yourself can be back here inside the hour. That ought to be the time we get the final blood count on the young man. And in the mean time Mary and Ellen here can scrub up the OR, just in case we need it.'

'Now wait a minute,' Mary interjected. 'Just because I let you handle all the social schedule doesn't mean that you can go around rearranging the nursing schedule. Ellen is going to ramble down the hall and get a good day's sleep. She was up all night. Terry can go along on this society thing. When she gets back we'll see how she feels about spending an hour under the light with you. After that she hits the sack. Tomorrow we'll have her on the duty roster. And in the mean time, Romeo—'

'Jim is the name, Major, ma'am.'

'In the meantime, Romeo, leave the little girl strictly alone. Terry, when I spoke about wolves, that includes our two doctors.'

'Why I think this one's very nice,' Terry replied demurely. 'He reminds me of my brothers. And besides, I make it a regular practice of eating an apple a day.'

'Of your brothers?' Jim snorted. 'I don't have any intention of reminding you of your brothers. An apple a day?'

'You know—an apple a day keeps the doctor away. And you'd better keep my brothers in mind. All five of them.'

'Okay, okay,' he chuckled, 'I'm suitably impressed.'

'How do I get to this Officers' Club?'

'There's a truck at the door, with a driver,' Jim Callagher said. 'But this is for the Base Commander. Why don't you take a minute or two to spruce up. Change your uniform?'

'I don't have anything to change to,' Terry responded.

'They've just brought your bags in,' Ellen reported. 'They've dumped them next door. Don't go fancy on us, though. White should be fine for a quick greeting.'

Terry stood up and stretched. Her skirt was wrinkled, and her blouse looked as if she had slept in it. Which I almost have, she teased herself. She waved to them all and went next door, closing the door gently behind her. My own little hidey-hole, she laughed to herself. You run to the end of the world and find yourself locked into another little cubicle. She shuddered, wrapped her arms around herself, and went over to the tiny window.

She was looking westward towards the shimmering ice of North Star Bay, but she saw nothing. His face was haunting her. Craggy, stern, with those grey eyes staring all the way through her, the laughter-lines gone from his full mouth, the tiny scar on his cheek throbbing under his thatch of light brown, straight hair. The way he had looked that last day in Houston before he stormed out of her life.

Terry shook herself out of her day-dream. She quickly moved her flight bag on to the bed and unzipped it. Among all the confusion of poor packing she managed to rescue a white trouser-suit that seemed almost unwrinkled. She eased herself out of her blue uniform, hanging the jacket carefully on the back of the chair. Slipping into the nurses' uniform was almost like donning protective armour. She zipped up the front of the blouse, then fumbled until she found a reasonably clean pair of white low-heeled shoes. She ran a comb through her tight black curls. As usual, they snapped back into exactly the same tight coils as before. She shrugged her shoulders, stretched up on tiptoes to see herself in the mirror, retouched her lipstick, and stepped out into the hall.

'Take my parka, Terry,' Ellen shouted after her.

'Hey. What's this?' Jim asked as he walked beside her down the corridor. He had taken her left hand in his, eyeing the gold ring that still circled her third finger. 'Oh my! Don't tell me they've slipped in a married ringer on us?'

She flashed her ring under his nose, being careful to ball her hand up into a fist so that only the ring could be seen, and not the scars. 'It must be a fake,' he complained, but he looked a little disappointed, and dropped off at the ward desk.

She almost felt like telling him that it was indeed a fake. What other woman would continue to wear that man's ring, continue to use his name, after all that had happened between them? Why would any sensible woman do that? But she knew the answer. Only a fool—only a love-sick fool.

As she passed through the airlock between the two sets of doors she snatched at Ellen's parka and put it on. It went around easily enough, but reached almost to her ankles. She pulled up the hood, wiggled her fingers into the double-insulated mittens, and stepped out into the cold.

'Better hurry up, ma'am,' the driver urged. 'We've had two radio calls already. The Old Man is getting a little ruffled.' He helped her up the high steps into the cab of the truck. They backed, turned, and started up the street at fifteen miles an hour.

Four blocks up, and three to the right, they turned off into a narrow parking area that looked as if it had been just cleared. Dirty snow was banked five feet high around its perimeter. The building set back behind the parking lot looked exactly like all the others. 'Inside there, ma'am,' the driver said. 'I'll wait for you. Dispatch said it would only take a few minutes.'

She scrambled down from the seat, reminding herself to avoid skirts while riding in trucks designed for long-legged men. She struggled up the path to the door of the building, trying to avoid loose piles of snow that swirled in the light breeze. The door opened from the inside.

'Lieutenant Alden?' a voice asked. She had heard it before on a radio circuit.

'Dr Fine?' she asked.

'Yes. Come in, please. We've only a few minutes before these people have to leave Thule. Their plane is waiting on the flightline now.'

He was a short man, barely four inches taller than Terry
herself. He was also a nervous man. His fingers kept
twitching, fumbling at the buttons of his semi-dress uniform. One lonely ribbon was stitched above his pocket. He
waited impatiently while she tugged her way out of Ellen's
over-large parka and hung it on an empty hook.

'Why me?' she asked him as she smoothed down her uniform blouse. 'I don't know anybody here.'

'It's your name,' he laughed. 'I was casually telling Colonel Hibbs about your prompt reactions on the aeroplane,
and he was struck by your name. Come on. They can't have
more than fifteen or twenty minutes to spare.'

He opened the second set of doors and she followed him
into the large room beyond. The outside of this building was
identical to all the others on the base, but inside there was
no interior panelling. The one large room looked like a huge
dark cave, with little spots of light from imitation candles set
on the scattered tables. After the snow-brightness outside
she had trouble adjusting her eyes to the gloom. All she
could discern was that there was a small gathering of people in front of her. One of them came over. She had the
impression of grey hair and a uniform jacket that bristled
with combat ribbons.

'Colonel Hibbs,' the doctor made the introductions. 'This
is our new nurse, Lieutenant Teresa Alden.'

'That's a remarkable coincidence,' the man in front of her
said. A hand reached out and grabbed hers. 'We've just got
a few minutes. They're running a bit late on their flight out
on to the ice-cap.' He continued to hold Terry's hand, tug-
ging her behind him into the still indistinct group. He pulled
her to a stop before a much larger figure.

'Lieutenant Teresa Alden,' the Colonel said, 'allow me to
present Dr Timothy Alden, from NASA.'

She caught her breath and her heart jumped into frantic
pounding action. She had no need to look all the way up to
that unchanged face. The grey eyes were like steel, the Ro-

man nose still aristocratically straight, his hair as unruly as ever. Terry shuddered and backed a step away, looking for some place to run, but the crush of other guests left her no place to go. She froze, her shoulders trembling, her hands clutching at the seams of her trousers. Surely, she told herself, he can't do it here. There are too many people around! Her eyes reflected her terror, she was too frightened to cry.

'Lieutenant Alden,' he said in that deep-timbred voice that had always thrilled her, and still did. 'What a surprising coincidence.'

And then he reached out with both hands under her armpits, lifted her up off the floor, and cradled her against himself, with his mouth to her ear. She struggled briefly, almost insane with fear, but the steel of those hands was too much for her puny muscles. Gradually she desisted, and both her feet dangled in air, waving vaguely.

'Well, Teresa,' he whispered in her ear. 'You've run to the end of the world and now I've found you. Where can you run now, little rabbit?'

Before she could marshal her wits he shifted her weight, swinging her up so that one of his arms was under her knees, and the other around her waist. His head loomed over hers, drawing her out of herself, making her respond as he always knew he could. She struggled, but her body betrayed her—as it always had with him. Her hands found their way around his neck, pulling his head down harder, forgetting the danger. She could feel emotions raging inside her, emotions she had stifled for six long years. But she could not control herself. She wove her fingers through his soft hair, and the struggle began in her stomach between fear and passion. And then suddenly he forced his way out of the crowd and carried her to the far corner of the bar, almost fifty feet away from the group.

He set her down on the floor in the middle of one of the tiny spotlit areas, illuminated by lights from over the bar. He was still holding her close, her nose squeezed against the cave where his ribs began. She had almost forgotten how tall he was.

'Lieutenant Alden,' he murmured into her ear. 'Still using my name? Not as proud as I, though, Teresa. I thought that by now you would have got rid of every image of me.' His voice was tinged with bitterness. He pushed her slightly away and stared at her. 'You've lost a lot of weight. And your eyes are tired. Life been too fast for you? Or is it the bottle that bothers you? Why are you shaking like that?'

'Because I'm—I'm afraid of you! Your mother brought me your message. Please—please let me go!'

'Let you go? After all these years? No, I'm not going to let you go, Terry. Not until I get an answer to my question. And don't tell me you've forgotten me!' One of his huge hands moved up and rested on her breast, fingering its softness under the thin shield of her blouse. She gasped, and cringed from him.

'See,' he chuckled. His hand moved down to engulf hers, bringing it up in front of his eyes. She struggled vainly to pull away. 'And you're even wearing my ring,' he said triumphantly. 'After all those years and you're still wearing my ring on—my God, Terry! What happened to your hand!' He was shaken out of his complacent mood. He spread the fingers of her left hand out, and stared at the scars running down the three fingers, and the stub of the little finger that was no longer there. 'What happened?' he demanded.

From across the room came a warning call. 'Time to go, gentlemen. We have to rush.'

He held her out at arm's length, all trace of the smile gone, his eyes hard. 'What happened?' he insisted.

She wiggled desperately, enough to break free from his hands, and backed, trembling, until the edge of one of the small tables pressed against her thighs, and stopped her retreat. And now the tears came. Her left hand, almost unconsciously, came up to her mouth, where her lips nibbled at its torn edges.

'What happened?' he insisted. The voice from the other end of the room repeated its warning call.

'Why keep torturing me?' she screamed at him. 'You know what happened! You happened! You and your loving mother. Damn you both! I wish I had never met you—either of you!' She turned and fled across the room, slipping and sliding on the highly polished floor, tears blinding her eyes. As she battered herself against the first set of doors she could hear him behind her.

'I'll be back shortly,' he called. 'I mean to have an answer, Teresa!'

As she grabbed at Ellen's parka, a pair of hands came out to help. Dr Fine was behind her. 'We'll have to hurry,' he said prosaically. 'That airman's blood work is in. Jim says he has to operate immediately. You all right?'

She nodded, biting back the tears. Get control of yourself, she commanded. Get control of yourself. This is exactly what he wants. He wants to see you tremble and shiver and cry before he does it. Wasn't that what his mother said? She found a tissue in the pocket of Ellen's parka and dried her eyes. Dr Fine, impatiently waiting at the door, signalled again. She followed him out to the waiting truck, where they fitted themselves on to the front seat, herself in the middle. The truck was held up while four staff cars carried away the VIP's. The doctor was squeezing himself against her more closely than space dictated, but she was too numb to reprove him.

'That certainly was a surprising meeting,' he probed at her. She ignored the statement, staring straight ahead. The truck jerked into motion. 'He didn't sound like a medical man. Doctor of Philosophy, I suppose. Did you know him from before?'

It was no use. There could be no hiding it. Not in such a small, isolated community. 'Yes,' she said softly. 'He's an Astrophysicist. We are—were—related.'

The little hospital was quiet when they returned, but people were moving quickly, with purpose. Mary met them at the ward desk. 'Everything go well?' she asked, and then didn't wait for an answer. 'Callagher has diagnosed appendicitis. He wants to operate within the half-hour. Do you want to take it?'

'Yes,' she almost shouted. It was something to do. Something to put her hands to, and keep her mind shuttered. 'Yes, I do,' she repeated more softly. 'But it's been a year since I've run a theatre. Do you keep your day-book on the instruments?'

'There's an Air Force manual for everything,' Mary commented drily. 'With pictures. Look in the Prep room. Gowns, books, gloves, everything.' She waved towards a door set at right-angles to the rest of the building. Terry shrugged her shoulders and hurried off. She found the right book at the top of the pile, and checked the picture layout of instruments for an appendectomy. Then she threw herself headfirst into the ritual of inspection, sterilisation, and checking.

By the time the two doctors appeared, the OR was spotless, and the instruments laid out in their tray in regimented order. She helped both to gown, then washed and put on her own gown and gloves. The patient was wheeled in, looking wan and listless from his pre-op shots, and oh, so young, she thought, so young.

And then the work began. A team of robots serving a single pair of hands. When it was over she made a careful count, watched the doctors leave, then dropped her mask and began the interminable job of clean-up. One of the wardmen came in to help. Wearily she struggled to the end of her check list, and then peeled off her paper gown.

'You look beat, Terry,' Mary said when she walked out into the open ward. 'Everything is in good hands here. The orderlies can watch things for a while. You could probably use a good belt of—'

'Please,' she begged. 'I'm just terribly tired. And I don't drink.'

'Not anything?'

'No, not anything.' She was being led down the hall to the nurses' quarters.

'So get yourself a hot shower and climb into bed,' Mary ordered. 'I'll make you a cup of—no, that damn coffee will keep you awake all hours. How about some tea?'

She nodded her acceptance. Half an hour later, warmed and relaxed by the hot shower, she put on her old-fashioned flannel nightgown and climbed wearily into bed. She had scrubbed and scrubbed, but her mouth still retained the imprint of his lips, and her breast seemed still dimpled by the pressure of his hand. She huddled down under the covers, trying to shake off her mood. A knock on the door heralded the arrival of the tea. The chief nurse set the mug down on the tiny table next to her bed.

'Try that,' she invited. 'There's milk and sugar, but I haven't added anything.'

Terry scooped up the mug and cradled it between her palms. She sipped gratefully at its warmth, and leant back against the pillows. 'And Jim Callagher says you'd better take these.' Mary handed her two white pills. Terry swallowed them without argument, and sipped more tea. Mary seemed to be reluctant to leave.

'You know,' the senior nurse said, 'the story is all over the base already.'

'What story?' she asked, not paying close attention.

'The story about you and this scientist at the Officer's Club. They're saying you jumped on this stranger and almost strangled him with a bear hug.'

Terry reached out her hand in supplication. 'It wasn't like that,' she said, and the tears came back again. 'It's not what you think. He's my—he was my husband.'

'Oh my,' the older woman exclaimed. She moved closer to the bed and held Terry against her comfortingly. 'If you look close you can see the marks of my shoe on my tongue. There now, girl, let it all hang out. Have a good cry.' And then she rocked Terry gently back and forth until the last tear had fallen.

'There's no need to worry, whatever,' the older woman continued. 'They've gone. They took off at midnight.'

'Do you know where they were going?' Terry pleaded.

'No. I have no idea. We medical people don't mix a great deal with the rest of the hired help. But he's gone. That make you feel better?'

'Yes—no—oh lord, I just don't know.'

'Want to tell me about it?'

'No. No, I can't. You wouldn't believe me if I did.'

'So he's chasing you? What does he want, an easy lay?'

'Oh God, please stop,' Terry cried. The tears had come again, in full spate. If that was all he wanted, she thought, all he would have to do is crook his little finger at me. God, how I ache for that man. If all he wanted was a quick tumble, I'd be in his bed so fast that—

'Then what does he want?' Mary probed. 'Does he have some kind of kinky quirk, or something?'

'No! Of course not. I just can't tell you. Please don't ask!'

The elderly nurse shrugged her shoulders, rearranged the covers over her, and went out, closing the door behind her.

Terry stared at the door, the mirror, the tiny picture of Miami, Florida, on the wall, and the tears rolled again. How can you tell someone—anyone—that the man you love wants to kill you?

CHAPTER TWO

TERRY WOKE UP in sunshine, after a restless sleep. She flipped back the covers and put her feet on the floor, groping for her sheepskin slippers. She made one effort to stand up, and then settled back against the pillows. It had been a sleep full of dreams, recollections, forced into her mind because she had seen him. And now all she could think of was that single year they had lived together, and how it had all started.

They had been adolescent sweethearts. He was a senior at New Bedford High School when they first met, she a beginner at the adjacent Junior High School. And she had loved him ever since. He had lived on Hawthorne Street with his widowed mother, one of the First Families of Massachusetts. She had lived down in the company houses on Hazard Street. 'The Blocks', they were known as in those days. She was the only daughter in a large Portuguese immigrant family. Her father had lived dangerously, in the fishing fleet.

Tim had come to her whenever he was home from the Massachusetts Institute of Technology. Her father had approved of him, and her mother had accepted him as one of the family. Terry had never met *his* mother. Until the day they came back from their two-day honeymoon at Old Sturbridge Village.

'You'll love her,' he said. 'And she'll love you!'

'But—does she know we're married?' Terry had stammered. She had been very shy in those days. With him she blossomed; with others she was tongue-tied.

'No,' he answered, 'she doesn't know. How could she? Even we didn't know, did we?'

'Well, I only came to see you get your Masters degree,' she exclaimed. 'How was I to know that—well, how could I know?'

'Swept you off your feet, did I? I always meant to do that.'

'But how was I to know that you had the marriage licence in your pocket under your gown. How could you know that I would—'

'I know everything about you,' he boasted. 'I even managed to get you to take a blood test for the application. And you never caught on, did you?'

'Sometimes you're very—very autocratic,' she returned. 'Sometimes I think—I—you have to leave me room to breathe, Tim.'

'I'm not holding you!'

'I mean—room for mental breathing. I have to have time to be me! Suppose I had said no?'

'Fat chance. I knew you'd do everything I told you to do. You always did. And you don't need to be you. Now you're part of me. Isn't that what the priest said—and you two shall be one? Here's the house. Smile, keep your chin up, and act like Mrs Alden, little rabbit.'

'I'll try. Honestly, I'll try. But—'

'No more buts. I know you're only seventeen, and have a lot to learn, but I'll teach you. Believe me.'

'Oh—I believe you, Tim. I'll do whatever you say. I love you.'

'That's more like it. Here we go.'

He led her up the graceful curved marble steps, and through the double front door of the old red-brick mansion. She followed, shifting her wide green eyes from side to side in awe. She had never conceived of such luxury, never mind seen it! His mother was waiting for them in the drawing-room, just to the right of the front door. She was tall, as he was, and slender to a fault. Her dress was watered silk, cut simply, her only ornament was a rope of pearls. Her white hair was blue-tinted. Tim made the introductions casually. Terry felt like falling through the floor. She was still dressed in the white cord slacks and plain cotton blouse that she had worn on their trip back. His mother examined her as if she were some sort of specimen from a biology class. They made small talk until his mother invented an errand for Tim, and when he had left the room, she walked around Terry, like an Indian looking for a place to attack the wagon train.

'I can't believe it,' his mother said. 'I just can't believe it. I knew he was a little wild, and chased a lot of skirts. But to marry a *Portagee* girl—and then have the nerve to bring you here! Are you pregnant?' In that quick exchange Teresa realised that she had found an enemy, and the façade of happiness which she had been building up for two days crumbled at its corners and collapsed.

Seven years ago, she told herself. And now you're twenty-four, and it's all behind you. Far behind you. Wearily she forced herself to get up. Her small travelling alarm clock said seven-thirty. She had nodded off just around two o'clock in the morning, and now it was morning again. She reached over to flip off the alarm, and forced herself to take a brighter outlook on life.

During her little nap someone had unpacked for her. She could see her uniforms hanging on an open pipe-rack in the corner. The old dressing gown which she had cherished for five years was thrown across the foot of the bed. She pushed herself up, feeling unaccountably weak, and wrapped the dressing gown around her. She flexed her stiff knees a couple of times, remembering with a chuckle the mad exercise cycles of basic training.

She walked over to the window. There was a bright glow which outlined everything. A series of snowbanks stretched from her window to a single long wharf, projecting out into the frozen ocean. The sky overhead was a brilliant blue, without a cloud to be seen. The world was a panorama of brilliant whites and blues. North to Alaska, she thought, and hummed a few bars of the old song. And then she was struck by the nonsense of it all. *South* to Alaska! She was already above the seventy-fifth parallel, and every part of Alaska lay to the south of her. Give or take a few guesses, she was idling in a steam-heated bedroom only nine hundred miles from the North Pole! She shrugged her shoulders and laughed. The end of the world, indeed!

Terry walked around the little room, fingering the furniture, learning with her tactile senses the boundaries of her new domain. Better get a shower, girl, she told herself. Sooner or later today someone will be wanting you for something. And you've probably missed a meal already.

She snatched up a towel from the top of the bureau, dug out her much-travelled shower kit, and went out into the hall. She turned the wrong way, towards the wards, then corrected herself, and clopped to the other end of the hall. The shower room was empty. She luxuriated under the plentiful hot water, and when she stepped out her skin was rosy. The steam had condensed on all the mirrors, so she rubbed a clear circle in one of them, and found, as usual, that it was set too high on the wall for her. She tried balancing on her toes, but could not maintain the stance. Faintly damning the world of tall people she dried herself, struggled back into her robe, and banged out into the tiny kitchen. Ellen was sitting by the table, mooning over a cup of coffee.

'Sleeping Beauty?' Ellen asked. 'Grab a mug. This coffee is left over from last night.'

Terry grinned at her. 'From last night? Do you save your coffee grounds for ever?' She walked over to the counter and poured herself a cup.

From the other end of the hall a male voice announced loudly, 'Man in the house!'

Ellen got up and opened the kitchen door. 'Down here,'
she called back. And then to Terry, 'It's the custom around
here. This end of the building is strictly woman's domain,
but it's not a convent. When there's a male inside the door
everybody has to know. What with the temperature always
at seventy degrees in here, some of us don't wear a lot of
clothes when we're off duty.'

'Hey, so this is where the off-duty staff is?' It was Jim
Callagher. 'You're looking much better, Terry.'

'I feel a lot better,' she answered. 'I don't want you all to
think I'm a weak sister. It was just that being up all night on
that flight, and then the shock of meeting—of meeting all
of you. It's surprising what a couple of hours of sleep will
do for a girl.'

Jim Callagher reached over and held her wrist. She felt
flustered, not sure whether he was staking a claim or taking
her pulse. He laughed at her confusion. 'Pulse is about
normal,' he chuckled, 'but I don't think I could classify that
nap of yours as a couple of hours. That was Monday night
when you went to sleep. Now it's Wednesday morning.'

'Wednesday?' Terry registered her astonishment. 'That
can't be! I've never slept that long before!'

'One of the advantages of owning your own hospital,'
Ellen interjected. 'The good doctor prescribed nembutal for
you, instead of aspirin. Boy, did you snore up a storm!'

Terry blushed. 'I never snore,' she started to say, and then
covered her mouth with her hand. That had always been one
of *his* complaints. 'When you're over-tired or worried, you
stretch out straight on your back and snore like a banshee,'
Tim had said.

'And the next thing the doctor prescribes for you is conversation,' the doctor continued. 'You're all wound up like
a top, Terry. You need to talk out your troubles. The more
you talk, the more you'll unwind. And for goodness' sake,
eat something. You need to gain fifteen or twenty pounds.'

He stopped to sip the hot coffee Ellen had provided for him. 'That's a medical opinion, of course.'

He turned his chair backwards and straddled it, leaning his long arms on its back. 'How did those doughnuts turn out?' he asked Ellen.

She walked over to the metal cabinet over the counter. 'A medical triumph,' she announced. 'The operation was a success, but the patient died. But if you think very little of your stomach you could try one of them.' She pounded a doughnut down on the table in front of him as if it were made of cast-iron.

'Terry,' he said quietly, 'we're a small community, and we try to look after each other. Don't flinch, for heaven's sake. Look at me.' He caught her chin in his hand, forcing her to look directly at him. 'I'm Jim Callagher, surgeon, husband, and father of three kids. My wife is five foot eight, and weighs one hundred and fifty pounds. Why should I want to chase around after a little bitty thing like you when I've already got a whole armful of woman?'

She half smiled at him, forced to participate in his good humour. 'I'm very happy for you,' she said. 'But I'm here, and she isn't.' Talk out her troubles? She was ready, eager to talk to someone. But talking about her troubles would bring relaxation, and that she dared not do. 'Are you going to eat the doughnut?' she asked.

'Of course I am. Just as soon as I get up the nerve. And don't change the subject. You can't let this—this man bug you,' he persisted. 'When you're ready to talk, we'll listen. By the way, I checked at Operations yesterday—your man has been making a nuisance of himself. He's been up here once a month since November. Claims he has to test the instruments for the International Geophysical Year. But that doesn't start for another four months. This doughnut isn't half bad, Ellen.'

'Half bad? What kind of a compliment is that?' Ellen asked.

Terry listened to their easy banter with half an ear. She was not prepared to accept criticism of Tim from any outsider, and yet she was curious—as curious as they were as to what might be going on. But before she could extract any more information the chief nurse broke up the meeting. She was bouncing with energy as she walked in.

'All hands to the barricades,' Mary announced. 'They've diverted a Nightingale Ambulance flight from West Germany to San Francisco on the Polar route. She'll be here in three hours. Every patient goes except the kid who just had the appendectomy. Terry, you get the prize. You and Dr Fine take the regular sick call. You've got fifteen minutes. Meet him in front of Ward One. Ellen, you start down the line with all those patients from the truck accident. Shots, treatments, case histories. I'll pull off both of the orderlies. They can share the graveyard shift tonight, and we'll use tomorrow, or until the next rush, for a complete clean-up and re-stocking.'

That announcement was the beginning of five days of hard work, as Terry pitched in with the others in a burst of housekeeping. The Air Base Squadron had furnished a detail of ten 'volunteers' to help with the heavy work. She enjoyed the job, and the repartee that accompanied it. In her spare time she read the Arctic Survival Manual, drew a complete set of arctic cold-weather gear, and made a tour of the base and its outlying stations.

The tour came about almost by accident. She had just come off night duty and was gobbling down at eight o'clock breakfast when Ellen came in, favouring one foot. 'Turned my ankle,' she complained, as she hobbled to a seat. 'Slipped on that ice patch at the front ramp, darn it. And I wanted to make the Grand Tour today.'

'The Grand Tour?'

'Sure. All the way around the perimeter of the base. We're getting ready for the influx of summer visitors. All during the winter we have a low incidence of respiratory diseases, but the minute the "tourists" start to arrive, they bring flu. So we run the Grand Tour, and get everyone innoculated. Would you like to make the trip for me, Terry?'

'Why, of course I will. What do I have to do?'

'Not much. Master Sergeant Enderson will drive and keep the records. All you have to do is use the gun on whoever shows up. He's waiting up front. Want to go?'

'What will Mary say?'

'Mary's taking a day off. That leaves me in charge, babe. How about it?'

And so she had gone, squeezed into an open jeep next to the elderly Master Sergeant who was the heart of the station's medical programme. The jeep slid and stuttered up South Mountain, depositing her at the Television State, where men from the mountain's several detachments had gathered. Terry administered shots for an hour, borrowed a cup of coffee, and started back down again. The Sergeant had stopped the vehicle at one of the swayback points on the mountain road.

'Take a look at that, Lieutenant,' he said, gesturing towards the north and east. 'That big cliff. See it? That's the edge of the Greenland ice-cap. In the summer all the snow between here and the cap will melt away, and you'll see flowers and streams and foxes and rabbits, but the ice-cap will stand there and glare at you without a change. See if you can get someone to take you over there in July. You might even see a bird or two. The ptarmigan come this far north as soon as the local ground cover clears.'

'You know what confuses me,' she returned. 'There's no natural sound! No birds, no bees, no—no nothing. All I can hear is that infernal thumping of the steam plant and the generator. And not a tree in sight. And that darn sun. Doesn't it ever really go down?'

'You're in the wrong season,' he laughed. 'The sun goes down for about forty minutes at this time of year. Come the fourteenth April and it's up twenty-four hours a day—until the twenty-first August, when it starts to set again. And when the sun is really up, you'll see this snow cover disappear almost overnight. And the flowers and grasses will be up and blooming almost like magic. But we'd better get going. There are a lot of men on North Mountain.'

The jeep clattered down the winding mountain path, crossed the relatively smooth roads of the base itself, and started up the other side. The whole top of North Mountain was flat. They gave injections for two hours, begged lunch from the Army detachment, and went back out into the sun again. Sergeant Enderson gestured across the flatland area of the mountain to the glisten of ice about a mile away. 'Wohlstenholme Fjord,' he identified it. 'And you notice the ice-cap comes right up to the cliffs around the fjord. In the summertime the ice-cap will start moving in this direction, and big chunks of it will fall off into the fjord. In about eighteen months those chunks will be icebergs floating down towards the ship-routes of the north Atlantic—'

'Where they'll sink the *Titanic*?' Terry laughed.

He smiled back at her. 'Exactly. Where they'll sink the *Titanic*.'

'We could walk across there,' she suggested. 'It's only three o'clock, and the fjord can't be more than a mile from here?'

'Distances are deceptive,' he laughed. 'The edge of the fjord is twelve miles from here. Take a look at that wire fence out there. How far out is that?'

'Oh, about two miles?' she guessed. It actually seemed to be half a mile away, but she was taking no chances.

'Not bad,' he commented. 'It's actually five miles out. That fence is out there to keep humans from wandering away.'

'So we won't pollute the ice-cap?'

'No—so we don't get lost. Right now the fence is only a landmark, but in the dark of winter, from the twenty-second

November until the fourth February, it's extremely important. This whole area is dangerous in the dark. And if you add a storm on top of the darkness, it can be fatal. That's the reason we wear these strips of luminous tape on the back of our parkas. By the way, there's one more sight to see.' He re-started the jeep and drove along the top of North Mountain to its western edge, which stood out like the prow of a tremendous ship.

'Look down there.' He pointed downwards to a plateau which stood out from the side of the mountain. 'That's the oldest Christian cemetery in the Arctic ocean area. A missionary named Hans Egede converted the Inuits in 1721. The local people claim that before the conversion they buried their leaders and shamans up there on top of Mount Dundas. I kind of doubt that—I don't see anyone getting up on Dundas without a helicopter. Well, we'd better get back, I suppose.'

They arrived back at the hospital just at five o'clock, half an hour before Mess call. Terry found it more convenient to come in the back door, and discovered Major Malson at the coffee pot with her feet up.

'Have a good day?' Mary asked.

'Wonderful,' Terry replied, patting at her wind-nipped cheeks. 'We saw North Mountain, and South Mountain, and all the scientific gadgets your heart could ask for—and only one casualty?'

Mary's ears pricked up. 'One casualty?'

'Yes. That big Lieutenant up at the TV station. The one who used to play football for Mississippi State? He was demonstrating to the troops that the injections didn't hurt. So I put the gun away and took out the needle. He fainted dead away, and it took us ten minutes to revive him. He's got a big bruise on his forehead, now. Oh my!'

'There's one in every crowd,' the major laughed. 'By the way, there's someone been waiting to see you. He came in about four o'clock. I told him you'd call him when you got back, but he insisted on staying. Said something about if you knew who it was you wouldn't call.'

'I—' Terry was too shocked to think straight. 'It's—'

'Yes, it's him. Want to see him? I'll come with you if you want.'

'I—' She gathered up all the bits and pieces of her courage. It was too late to run. There was no place to go. A dull fatalistic cloud settled over her, washing away the laughter and happiness of the day. 'I—could I bring him down here?'

'Are you afraid of him, Terry?'

'Yes. But I guess I have to talk to him sometime. You'll stay with me?'

'Yeah. There are times when an old battle-ax comes in handy. Sit still. I'll go bring him down. Get yourself a cup of coffee. Or take a nip of my brandy—it's on the second shelf, behind the sugar can.'

Terry was still fumbling with her coffee cup when they came in. Major Malson pulled out a chair at the second table, a few feet away from them, and sat down. The man glared at the major. She glared back.

Terry just stared. In the brightness of the kitchen's fluorescent lights she could see that he had changed. He was as tall and firm as always, but his face was thinner. He had added another scar to the side of his face, a small red line running from the corner of his eye to his right ear. His sandy hair still strayed, and the cowlick still kept falling down over his eyes. She had the insane urge to go over to him, to brush it away, to—

'I'd like to talk to my wife alone,' he said coldly to the chief nurse.

'We—we're not married any more,' Terry interjected quickly.

'That's one of the things we have to talk about,' he replied.

'Well, go ahead, talk,' Mary told him. 'I need a good story to liven up the day.'

'I didn't come all this way to liven your day,' he snarled.

Major Malson gave him a chilly smile. 'I know you didn't,' she said. 'Why don't you go ahead and talk. I've got two male orderlies on duty at the reception desk, and the AP detachment is right across the street. Go ahead, talk.'

'Terry,' he appealed to her. 'We need to talk. Alone. Can't you get rid of this—'

'No. I asked her to stay.' He moved towards her. Terry tensed, and backed away until she bumped into the serving counter. 'Don't—don't come any closer,' she pleaded.

'What the hell is the matter with you,' he exploded. 'You act as if I was a plague bearer or something.'

'I—please, don't,' she repeated.

'Teresa?' His voice was softer. He had decided to persuade, not threaten. 'I have to talk to you. It's been six years. I've looked for you everywhere!'

'I know,' she replied. 'I learned to avoid your detectives.'

'If not here, how about having dinner with me at the Club? They serve a good meal, there'll be a big crowd, and we can talk privately. All I want to do is talk to you, Teresa.'

'You mean that's all you want to do right this minute!' There was an edge of fear and scorn in her voice.

'So all right,' he smiled, 'I do have other ideas. But all I want to do right now is talk. How about it? Dinner?'

'I—' She looked at Mary with an appeal in her eyes. The older nurse nodded agreement.

'I—well, all right. But we just talk. No funny business!'

'What kind of funny business could I pull in that place? I'll pick you up in about an hour. Six o'clock, say?'

'No! I told you. I'll meet you at the Club at six if that's what you want. But you're not picking me up—and you're not bringing me back. I won't go any place where I'll be alone with you. You understand?' Her statement lost its impact as her voice squeaked on the last four words.

He shook his head in disgust. 'No, I don't understand,' he said, 'but I'm trying to. I've been trying to understand for six years, Terry, and I still don't. But we have to make one more side trip, and then we're flying out for the summer. Well, if that's all I can get, I'll meet you at the Club at six o'clock. And leave your watchdog behind.' He turned and stormed off up the corridor.

Terry staggered to the table and sat down, spilling half of her coffee over her uniform. Both hands were trembling. She grounded the cup and clasped her hands together, trying to still them.

'Nice-looking man,' Mary offered.

'Yes,' Terry stammered. 'Nice.' Her hands strangled the coffee mug. Lord, how he's changed, she thought. He was always explosive, always possessed of a terrible temper, shooting off like a rocket. When they were first married she had always waited until he spoke first, so that she could judge his temper. But now, although he looked harder, he seemed to be more controlled. Older, of course—maybe that was it. He looked knocked about, too. That was something new. Always before he had been the lucky one. He went to the best schools, joined the best clubs. All that and the Mayflower, too! Had she been jealous? Had she married him because of that aura he wore—that aura of importance, of heritage, of money? Proud of him she had been. Always wanting to show him off to her girl friends. Like a kid with a toy, she mused. Or the other way around, more than likely. She had been his slave. 'I guess men ought to be warned never to marry their slaves,' she mumbled. 'But lord, how I loved him then!'

'Past tense,' Mary asked.

'I—I don't know,' she sighed.

'Well, go get gussied up. Wear your dress blues. Put on a little perfume. Wear a tight blouse. It's all allowed in the Regulations. Come to think of it, I'll just stir Jim Callagher out of his nightly chess game, and get him to take me to dinner at the Club, too!'

'Major Malson, ma'am?'

'Yes?'

'You're a fraud. A soft-hearted fraud!'

'You may be right, Teresa, but it took you a week to find out, didn't it. Scramble. Try a little make-up, too. It's all allowed in the Manual.'

As it turned out there were four of them to walk the few blocks to the Club for dinner. The sun was still high and bright. Not only had Mary collected Jim Callagher, but she had added Captain Harry Engels to her party. Harry was the commander of the Air Police detachment.

'Harry's the pride of Thule society,' Mary said as she introduced them. 'He's the only bachelor officer on the base—or at least the only one who will admit it. And darned good company. Played football at Yale University.'

'Harvard, ma'am,' he insisted. 'Harvard. And available for baby-sitting, hand-holding, company for the elderly—'

'And the protector of fair maidens?' Terry laughed up at him. 'Don't you three goons think you're fooling me a bit. Did you bring your gun and club, Captain?'

'No. To tell you the truth I didn't think about that. Should I go back and get them?'

'Please!' She was enjoying the teasing, but it was getting out of hand. 'I don't think—in all this crowd he—'

'He what?' the captain asked firmly.

'He nothing. He won't do anything. We're just going to talk. It's been a long time since we were divorced. We're civilised people.' But she knew it wasn't true. His mother had been very explicit about what he intended to do. She had no illusions.

There was a bustle at the door, with several parties dropping off their heavy outdoor equipment at the same time, and then she was inside. It was slightly cooler than the hospital, with the only light coming from the individual lamps on each table, and a few tiny spotlights over the bar. She pulled down the hem of her short mess jacket, and a hand touched her shoulder. She jumped, and took a step away from him. Tim looked at his hand, hanging in mid-air, with a quizzical glance. Then he lowered it.

'I've a table over here.' He gestured towards the far corner. She nodded. He started to take her arm, then thought better of it. Terry followed his giant stride across the floor, remembering with a small sigh all the times and places where she had chased him across rooms. He seemed to have read her mind. He stopped, glanced back at her, and then proceeded more slowly.

Tim helped her into a chair, and then, rather than sitting across from her on the other side of the small square table, he took the chair adjacent to hers. Out of the corner of her eye she could see Mary and her convoy guards settling into another table a few feet away.

'Terry?' His voice snapped her out of her wonderland. 'I ordered a couple of drinks for us,' he said. 'As I remember, it was gin and tonic, wasn't it?'

'I—I don't drink,' she returned apologetically. 'I don't drink anything alcoholic. They have a nice lemon and lime drink, if you wouldn't mind?'

'Lemon and lime?' he asked in amazement. 'You *have* changed!'

Her temper snapped as he flicked her on the raw edge of memory. 'It was only once!' she snapped. Her face turned red and she half raised her left fist at him. 'It was only once! But you wouldn't believe me then, and you don't believe me now, do you!' She threw her challenge at him with a glare in her eyes, and her little jaw stuck out as far as it could go.

He stared at her for a moment, then raised his arm to attract a waiter. 'No, I didn't believe you then,' he said quietly. 'But I was pretty much a fool in those days. Just a macho kid. And some sort of a dictator where you were concerned. Tell me what happened.'

She studied him carefully, trying to spot the trap in his words, but his face was unreadable. 'It was my birthday,' she recalled. 'My eighteenth birthday. You don't remember, do you? You didn't then, either. You were in Florida for the moon shot. You didn't even call me. God, I was so lonely. You had told me to mix with the other wives. When Alice called me—Alice Harrington?—I thought I was doing what you wanted me to do. She invited me over for drinks. I had been so full of—of self-pity, and I hadn't eaten all day. She served some fruit punch, and I didn't know what was in it. All I remember is that when I started to go home, I couldn't walk. So she offered to drive me home. I got out of her car—I guess it must have been eight o'clock at night, or thereabouts—well, I got out of the car, and managed to stumble up the stairs to the front door, but I couldn't find the key. So I sat down on the stairs to catch my breath, and I guess I must have fallen over, because—'

'Yes, I remember that part. When I came home the next morning you were fast asleep in the flower bed, with the hem of your dress up around your neck some place, and all the neighbours looking and laughing.'

She looked over at him with a tear forming in the corner of her eye. 'I was too young, Tim,' she sighed. 'You should never have married me. Or at least you should never have left me alone for so long. I was so lonely.'

The waiter brought their drinks. Tim puzzled over this, drawing little circles on the high polish of the table. 'I thought I was doing the right thing,' he said finally. 'I guess I was just swept up in the excitement. Having a job in the Moon programme was like having one foot in the future. I thought that it would last for a few years, and then we would settle down. Funny thing. If I could have shared my work, boasted about it, maybe, it would have helped tie us together. But I couldn't even do that. All the stuff I worked on was classified "Secret".' He stopped and gulped half of his drink. For some reason, as he talked, her hand had wandered halfway across the table, and now his huge one came down on it and squeezed hers gently.

'You said I would never believe you. Well, you're wrong. I do believe you. I would have then, too, except for my damn temper and stiff-necked pride. All I could see was the neighbours laughing at you, and that—that damn bikini underwear you used to wear, revealed right there by the street! I know you must have been scared. I was a great help to you that day, wasn't I?' He was being sarcastic. The corner of his mouth had turned upwards in his usual expression of disgust. 'We were both too young, Terry. Too young.'

They sat quietly. A three-piece band had begun background music at the far end of the room, and the place was rapidly filling up. Her eyes returned to him. She leaned over the table towards him, unconsciously stretching out her hand to brush the cowlick back from his forehead. He stiffened as her fingers slid across his brow. Recognizing at last what she was doing, she drew her hand back, only to find it trapped in his. She did not flinch, did not draw back. He lowered their joined hands to the table, his heavy thumb tracing diagrams on her outstretched right palm.

'If we were too young then,' he murmured persuasively, 'how about now? How do you think it would be if we were married now?'

'I don't know, Tim,' she sighed. 'It was all such a waste. I loved you so much in those days. I would have gone through hell for you, barefoot. I think I did. If we were married today? If we could start all over again, without the past coming between us, without my stupid fears, or your mother's—I suspect we could have been very happy. But it's all too late, isn't it. There are too many barriers between us. God knows you divorced me fast enough, didn't you!'

'How did you know that?'

'How? Your mother came to the hospital and told me. The day after they amputated my little finger, can you believe that! God, how she hated me! And I don't know why, Tim. I didn't know then, and I don't know now. Why did she hate me so? The very first day we met she called me a *Portagee* bitch. And she never stopped. Why, Tim?'

'My mother called you that? Why didn't you tell me?'

'What? Me tell you something in those days? I never had the nerve! What a laugh that must have been to you. I loved you to desperation, but I was scared to death of you! Well, your mother straightened me out, let me tell you. She forced her way into the recovery room and took great pains to explain to me all about the divorce. And then she gave me your message. I was so frightened I discharged myself from the hospital.'

'And you've never stopped running, have you?' His voice was gentle, soft.

'No,' she responded bitterly. 'I've never stopped.' She sipped at her drink again, watching for his reaction to her next question. 'Did you ever marry the girl, Tim?'

'Marry? What girl?'

'The one your mother told me about. I don't remember her name. She was just right for you, your mother said. Society, education, money, sophistication. I remembered that because she seemed to be a list of all the things I was not. And that's why you divorced me so quickly—so you could marry this other girl. Or so your mother said.'

'My mother told you all that?' He seemed to sigh deep inside, to withdraw into himself. 'No, I never married anyone else, Teresa.'

They were interrupted by the waiter, bringing fresh drinks and dinner. Terry sagged back in her chair and caught her breath. It had taken all her courage to talk to him. And as she watched him casually attacking his steak, her heart began to pound and her dry throat tightened. She gulped down her drink.

'You're not eating?' Tim asked.

How can I eat? she wanted to scream at him. How can I eat with you here? But her long years of practice came to her aid. She smoothed her face into the placid calmness that had become her stock-in-trade, and began on her own meal. It tasted like cardboard. She smiled at him and forced the food down.

'Want some dessert?' he asked, when their empty plates had been taken away.

'No,' she answered, 'just coffee. It all seems so—so impertinent, ordering dessert on the edge of the Arctic Ocean. We brave explorers.'

'Don't knock it,' he laughed. 'You should come out with me if you want to see some real survival living. There's plenty of it left out there. Care to come?'

'Me? I—I couldn't do that!' she gasped. Some of her fear of him was returning. 'It would be too much of a shock for a hot-house flower like me.'

There was a look of disbelief on his face. 'It's funny,' he said, 'I can't seem to read your face any more. It was always an open book—now the book is closed. I wouldn't dream of inviting the old Terry Alden out on to the ice. She was a rabbit. But you—you're different. Tell me something about you. What happened to the man you were living with in New Bedford?'

'The man I was—' Her face turned brilliant red. 'What man?'

'Oh, come on, Terry, we're all grown up now. My mother saw you several times, coming and going from the house on Maple Street—and with a man old enough to be your father. He put you in the hospital, didn't he? What did he do, beat up on you?'

She picked up her water glass and sipped at it to gain time. When she put it down her lips were smiling, but her eyes were cold. 'You're lucky you have such a wonderful mother,' she hissed at him. 'He was my father-figure. And he was old enough to be my father. In fact he *was* my father. What in God's world were you thinking of me? I went home to my father. Where else could I go, with a broken hand. I went home to my father, damn you!'

She struggled up from her chair, tears flowing. There was a stir at the adjacent table, but before anyone else could intervene he was up and at her side, cradling her head against the soft wool of his jacket. She turned into him, resting herself against his strength, drawing from the wells of his reserve the courage she did not have for herself. The warmth of him, the comfort, the familiarity, were all a part of what she needed. For the first time in years she relaxed, leaning close all along his muscled figure, shuffling her feet to bring herself closer. And eventually the tears stopped. He helped her back to her chair, and watched as she fumbled in her tiny purse for a tissue.

She managed to dry her eyes, then flashed a quick look into the mirror of her compact. 'I look a mess,' she muttered. 'I'd better find the powder room and—' He stopped her with one word.

'Don't,' was all he said. She looked deep into his eyes, and slowly tucked tissue and compact back into her bag. Then she set the bag aside and folded her hands at the edge of the table.

'Then there was never anyone else?' he asked.

She shook her head. How could she tell him. There had been a man in Denver. She had dated him for six weeks, thinking he might be the one. But one clear night when he had brought her back to the tiny apartment, he had stepped out of his car into the moonlight, and she had suddenly realised what attracted her to him. He looked like Tim! The way he held his head proudly, the arc of his chin, the way his deep-set eyes sparkled. He looked like Tim! She had never dated him again.

'No,' she murmured. 'There's been nobody, Tim.'

There was a long period of silence. 'Your mother has a lot to pay for,' she finally said.

He took her hand. 'She paid for it,' he answered. 'She died three years ago of cancer.'

'I—I'm sorry,' she said. 'Sorry for you. You loved her very much. I wish I could have understood her.'

'I never did understand her myself until a few minutes ago,' he returned. 'Some day I'll explain it to you.' His voice trailed off, and she could see that he was no longer with her. The waiter bustled her up with the coffee. Terry sipped at the dark brew and watched the man across the table until he shook his head, as if clearing away cobwebs, and smiled at her.

'Isn't it a coincidence that we should meet here after all these years?' she offered. There was a faint hesitancy in her tone, a doubt.

'You know better than that, don't you!' he answered harshly. 'I've spent seventeen thousand dollars in six years trying to find you. All kinds of detectives, all kinds of schemes. And then you fell right into my lap. Coincidence?'

'I—I don't understand.'

'You understand, Terry. You always were a rabbit, but never a dummy. When did you apply for duty up here?'

And then, suddenly, she understood more about herself than she wanted to know! She had been one of six graduates of the Officers' course who still had no assignment. When the Career Counsellor called her into his office at Kelley Field she had no idea what she wanted to do. In almost a joking fashion she had said, 'What I really would like to do is find some isolated place—the end of the world, I suppose. Do we have an air base there?'

'Have we ever,' he had laughed. 'But it's a classified base.'

'What does that mean, as far as I'm concerned?'

'It means that's it's cold, dark, and you have to file for a security clearance before you can be accepted. Here, take this form and fill it out.'

She had carried the four pages over to the table by the window, with the brilliant Texas sun shining in on her, and had struggled to fill in all the lines. It wanted to know everything. Every last address where she had ever lived, the name of every school she had ever attended, political affiliations, unions, clubs, visits abroad, names of six references (not relatives included). She had stumbled through most of them with little trouble, until she had reached the block labelled 'Marital Status'. Carefully she had printed in all the information she could remember, adding 'divorced' under the heading of 'Present Status'. The next line bothered her. 'Name and Address of Present or Former Spouse.' Her hesitant hand had scribbled in 'Timothy Albert Alden—address unknown.' She got up, meaning to hand the completed form to the counsellor, and then had second thoughts. She sat down again, struck out the 'address unknown' remark, and in a bold hand printed 'NASA, Houston, Texas.'

She stared at him now. 'You mean the FBI really came to check up on me?'

'Yes, they came,' he said. 'So naturally I knew where you were going, but not when. What was it, some sort of death wish?'

She winced at the appropriateness of the words he had used. Death wish? Or had she really, subconsciously, wanted a confrontation? Had she just been tired of running, or overfilled with longing? She drew back from the coldness of his eyes, the sternness of his mouth. She fumbled for something different to say, something to divert him.

'At least you didn't spend *all* your time looking for me. I see that you got your Ph.D.'

'Yes. In between bouts of insanity I managed to study a little. And by working in the Moon programme I had a ready-made thesis to hand. But that's not what I want to hear, Teresa. Look at me.' His hands cupped her chin and turned her head up. 'The one thing I don't have an answer for. That I never did have an answer for. Why did you run off and leave me?'

She struggled to break away from his hand. When the contact broke she moved as far away from him as she could. 'You knew,' she snarled at him. 'Your mother knew, and what she knew you did too!'

'Not true. I didn't know. Tell me now!'

Her anger was slowly building higher and higher. 'Why are you doing this to me, Tim? I know that you knew.'

He leaned towards her, placing his hand, palm up, on the table between them. 'Tell me anyway, then!'

'I'll tell you—you bastard,' she hissed at him. Slowly, with exaggerated movements, she laid her hand in his, palm up, so that the light reflected from all the angry little lines that jumped out at him. 'You did that to me,' she whispered.

'I did that?' He sat up straight, but did not release her hand. 'I never did anything like that, Terry! You know I didn't!'

'I know you did,' she told him relentlessly. 'You and your great stage exits. Walk off and slam the door in the girl's face. God, how I remember them all. And that front door in Houston, all solid oak with a metal trim. Remember that? The last time you walked out and slammed the door on my my hand was still in the door jamb!'

He dropped her hand as if it had been a rattlesnake, and his deeply-tanned face turned pale. 'My God, Teresa,' he groaned. 'My God! I never knew!'

'You knew,' she snarled back at him. 'The neighbours said I screamed for an hour before the ambulance came. They all heard. How could you help but know!'

They both sat up straight, frozen in position, two deadly antagonists facing each other in the arena. Neither spoke. The waiter came by and re-filled their coffee cups just as the little band struck up with 'The Eyes of Texas Are Upon You'. The music filtered into their minds, struck the same point of the grotesque in each of their minds, and released the tension. They both slumped, and a little smile flickered at the corners of her mouth.

'All right, Teresa,' he said solemnly. 'You've given me a setdown. You must know I'm sorry. I never did know. There doesn't seem to be anything else I can say about that.'

'There isn't,' she acknowledged. 'I've learned to live with it.' But not without you, her mind screamed at him. I'll never learn to live without you!

Tim used his fingers to stir a few more circles on the top of the table, then he looked up at her with a passion on his face that struck her dumb.

'There's one other thing you have to know,' he said, 'and then I have to go. I don't know what you may have heard from my mother, Teresa Maria, but I've never divorced you. You're still my wife!'

CHAPTER THREE

'BUT THE STRANGE THING about it is how much he's changed, Ellen.' Terry made another tick mark on the barbiturates list, and reached deeper into the cupboard for the next box. 'I can't really say how. It's just that he's different. Of course he's older—six years is a long time-but there's a sort of feeling I experienced, as if all his goals had changed. Can you imagine that? And he actually asked me to tell him something, and he listened. That never would have happened before. He was always the master, and I did what he told me to!'

She climbed down from the step-stool and pushed it into the corner. 'That's the last of them. Shall I lock up?'

'Yes,' Ellen said, squeezing in her first word in fifteen minutes. 'Lock everything, and then put the keys in the ward key-cabinet. So he was different? And you're still married? Are we going to see a grand reconciliation?'

'No! Nothing like that. I was just—thinking. No, we've gone our separate ways for a long time. And besides, he still—No! I don't expect anything like that.'

'And now what happens?'

Terry dropped the key-ring in her pocket, wondering the same question herself. They had met, and they had talked. Some things had been clarified, but nothing had been settled. She thought back to that look on his face when she had told him about her hand. It seemed almost impossible that he would not have known, and yet— Maybe he didn't, she concluded. And despite all that his mother had said, he had not divorced her. Or so he said. Did he have anything to gain by telling her a lie? Her mind whirled to no conclusion, and she gave it up.

'He said he had to go off on a training mission. I don't know exactly what that means, or where they've gone. Things were so—so tense, you know, that I didn't feel like asking him too much. That was four days ago, and I haven't heard anything. I don't even know if he's ever coming back.'

'Well, if he does, babe, why don't you whip out a fancy nightgown and move in on him? Or are you too scared?'

Terry stared reflectively at the other woman. 'Now why would you say that?' she laughed. 'You know, in all that year we lived together I never once wore a nightgown when he was home!'

'So he was good for something then, huh?'

Terry blushed and turned away, trying to find more work for her hands. For want of something better, she started restacking the rolls of elasticised bandages. Good for something? After that first wild night, oh how good it had been. She had never conceived in all her short life that there could be pain so sharp, or pleasure so intense, as their coming together. And over the months, step by step, they had mastered the art of pleasing each other. She shuddered at the thought, at the long years of abstinence, at the fires she had to bank!

'If you stack those things one more time we'll have to throw them out as used,' Ellen commented at her elbow. 'Besides, my maidenly unmarried ears are shocked by this whole conversation. Well, my unmarried ears, then.'

Terry shook the memories out of her mind and smiled an apology. 'Sometimes I get lost in time,' she said softly.

'Somebody's lost?' Dr Fine was at the door. 'Who's next on the duty roster?'

'Me,' Terry answered hesitantly.

'Okay. This will be an overnight trip off-base. We had been hoping for a chance to send someone, and now a chopper has to go out to pick up this scientific crew, so we'll make use of the free trip. You'll need your warmest clothes. Don't plan on any comforts. No running water, no baths. Grab a toothbrush and—Ellen, you tell her. You've made more than one outside trip.'

'For overnight you only need a change of underwear,' Ellen advised. 'But you could get stuck by a weather change. Long johns, you understand—all your thermal gear. Don't wear anything tight. No belts, no bra, and use those braces you were issued with. Felt slippers inside your mucklucs.'

'But I—'

'To keep warm you must have several layers of loose clothes. Nothing constricting, but three layers at least. No one will notice if you bounce a little. And put some of that special cream on your cheeks and lips.'

'Yes—and as fast as you can, and then come to the office,' the doctor interjected. 'I have someone for you to meet, and then I'll explain the problem. Ellen, are the vaccines in the refrigerator?'

Terry rushed to her room and dug out the light multi-layered cover-all sets which she had been issued with but never used. She stripped quickly, discarding everything but her favourite briefs. Then she began the ordeal. A two-piece set of thermal underwear, cover-alls, two sets of sweaters, and a set of insulated over-pants. She began to feel like an inflated balloon. Putting on her foot-liners, slippers, and mucklucs was almost more than she could handle. Her watch indicated that twenty minutes had passed. She hurried down the corridor, wiping perspiration from her brow.

Dr Fine was waiting for her, standing by an Inuit dressed casually in flannel shirt and fatigue trousers. He was about five foot four, but built widely, and heavily muscled. His bronze skin was lined with cracks, and his black eyes sparkled at her.

'Lieutenant Alden, this is Ungarlak. You and he are going on a trip,' Dr Fine said by way of introduction.

'We are?' Her voice squeaked in alarm. 'How do I—I've read about—I can't speak any—'

The Inuit laughed at her, showing a wide circle of brilliant white teeth. 'You read too many books, huh?' he asked. 'I speak American pretty good. I spend six years in Texas. You ever be in Texas?'

'Yes,' she gasped. 'I—yes. I lived in Houston!'

'Houston? Hey, great! They got some damn fine women in Houston. Say, you call me Charlie, huh? In the States I spend two years in the Army paratroopers. Everybody calls me Charlie.'

'But I thought your name was Ungarlak?'

'Made-up,' he shrugged. 'My father gives every boy a name of hope, you understand. Me, he calls Ungarlak—that means Great Seal Hunter. I never shoot a seal in my life. So we go to Etah together, huh?'

'Nurse Alden knows nothing about it yet,' Dr Fine interjected. 'What we have, Teresa, is a project to assist the government of Greenland. There are only five families still living in Etah, in the old style. Living from their hunting and fishing.'

'Most everybody else moves south to Gothaab,' Charlie added. 'Why hunt for seal when the codfish are running up the channel. Me and my three brothers, we own two motor boats, to take the cod and smoke it and sell it in Denmark for money. Everybody does this in Greenland these days. Except for the families at Etah. They hang out in the old way.'

'Don't knock it,' the doctor chuckled. 'If it's all that bad, how is it that this is the fifth time you've come north for the summer, to live off the seal?'

'So maybe I get lucky,' the Inuit responded. 'For vacation you statesiders go fishing, swimming, touring. Me, I go seal hunting. Some day I get one—and then maybe I don't go any more. Maybe.'

'But I—what do I do in Etah?' Terry stammered. 'I've never *seen* a seal, never mind hunted one.'

'It's nothing like that,' the doctor said. 'One of the families at Etah has decided to come south. Father, mother, and seven children. They've lived in isolation all their lives. When they go south they'll run into the white man's diseases. Especially measles. Without preparation, a case of measles could kill them. So you go up there and inoculate them all. You stay around for a few hours to check for reactions. And that's it.'

'But why all this rush?' she asked.

'Because we don't have any budget money to make the trip at all, and NASA does. They've got a couple of men up at Etah now, taking a survival course out on the ice. And they can afford a helicopter—and you hitch a ride with them. Simple?'

'Oh yes,' she sighed. 'You don't know who they are—these people from NASA?'

'No. Are you ready to go?'

'We go right after we take the first lesson in survival here,' the Inuit interrupted. He swept a big red bandana from his rear pocket and wiped her perspiring brow. 'First law. Never sweat! Never go so fast or so far that you sweat. Always unbutton the clothes to avoid it, huh. You lose liquids, huh. It freezes on you. Very dangerous. Frostbite. You know?'

An hour later they were on the flightline, standing by the base's only helicopter, a well-worn *HU 1F*. Much to Terry's surprise, when the pilot came out of the Ready room to introduce himself, it was like meeting her grandfather. He was a short and relatively stout man, with a fringe of white hair over a gleaming scalp, which he covered quickly with a fur-lined flight cap. His eyes twinkled at her as he noted her surprise. 'Gorton is the name,' he said. 'Major John Gorton. It's an old aircraft. So they need an old pilot. Make sense?'

'Why—of course, sir,' she laughed. She walked with him as he went around the helicopter on his pre-flight inspection. 'You must know how it is in the Air Force,' he commented as he tested the tension on some control cables. 'You're either up and at a desk at my age, or you're stuck in some backwater, flying aircraft as old as you are. I never had the brains to fly a desk. And I love all these old birds.' He patted the side of the chopper affectionately. 'So we're off to the wild reaches. Etah?'

'Siorapaluk!' the Inuit corrected him. Major Gorton turned around.

'You mean two-gun Charlie is your escort? Better be careful, Lieutenant. He's the original arctic fox. He still believes in the old tradition that a householder must share his women with visitors!'

Charlie appeared to be not the least upset. 'Climb aboard,' he directed her. 'Harry and me are old friends. He is the perfect example of the old saying.'

She could not help laughing at them, two short strong men, each a perfectionist in his own field, jibing at each other. 'What old saying?' she asked, looking as innocent as possible.

'Very famous saying,' Charlie repeated. 'We have old pilots, and we have bold pilots, but we have no old bold pilots. Chicken Little gets us there okay. Hurry up, Harry. See if you can make this thing go, huh?'

'Have to wait,' Gorton shouted over the rising engine noises. 'Tower says there are some windstorms locally. Could bring on a white-out.'

'Bah! Windstorms!' the Inuit complained. 'You people never learn. The white-out is cause by the *Qivitoq*, the monsters who live in the ice caves. They can fly by sitting down and extending one leg. And when they do, the snow moves!'

'What in the world are you both talking about?' Terry pleaded. They took pity on her.

'When there's a ground-level windstorm,' Major Gorton explained, 'it picks up all the loose dry snow and fills the air with it. To a pilot in the air the blowing snow merges with the landscape, and he can lose track of where he is. He loses everything—sense of direction, horizons, everything. And it happens very suddenly. If we were in a landing pattern it could mean plenty of trouble.'

'Don't worry. I got a certain cure,' Charlie assured them. 'I got this from the *Angekok*, the witch doctor. Guaranteed to settle white-outs by scaring the *Qivitoq*. Take a sample.' He passed the bottle over to the pilot, who took a small sip and started to cough.

'Damn,' the major said. 'It tastes like bourbon!'

'Well, even *Angekok* has to turn to modern materials sooner or later,' Charlie told him blandly.

For answer the major gunned the turbine engine, talking briefly to the controller in the tower, and pulled the helicopter almost straight up in the air. Terry gasped as they barely skimmed the top of the North Mountain, and made a great curve out over the grey expanse of Smith Sound.

'No place to land on the coast or on the ice-cap,' the major yelled into her ear, 'so we travel over the ocean. As long as it's iced over, this is the safest place to be. Look there now, straight ahead of us, behind the fjord. That's Inglefield land. The village is there just above the rocks. It's only a thirty-minute trip by air, one day by boat in the summertime, and one week by dog-team if you have to go over the glacier!'

They made one pass over the Inuit village. It sat on a rough ledge about twenty feet above the level of the ocean, with a sharply inclined slope down to the beach itself. Huge boulders, each ten to fifteen feet high, were scattered across the little plateau. Barely visible in the snow drifts she could see twelve scattered wood-and-sod houses. Only a few had an eddy of smoke wandering from the metal stove-pipes that served as chimneys. The buildings were unpainted, and weathered almost enough to match the boulders that sheltered them from the wind.

'Not so many people,' Charlie yelled in her ear. 'One by one, everybody goes south. Look on beach. Three years you see fifteen, maybe twenty boats, huh!' Terry peered out of the side window as the helicopter swung over the snow-covered beach. A line of five *kayaks*, the hunter's one-man boats, were overturned in a row, held off the snow by a pile of rocks at each end. At the far end of the little beach a much larger *umiak*, a family boat, was similarly placed. There were no dogs in the area, and no sleds.

The helicopter made a routine landing, sending up a swirl of snow as it bumped on to the ground. Two dozen people, indistinguishable in their furs, came to greet them, and to escort them into the larger of the houses, close by. Stepping through the slatted wooden door was to go from brilliant sunlight to almost darkness. A few pinpricks of light came from open dishes, with multiple lighted wicks soaked in whale oil.

Once inside, the Inuits immediately began to discard their outer gear. The house was warm, but the heat was compounded by the smell of unventilated humans. When the man in front of her began to take off his trousers Terry fixed her eyes steadily on her medical bag, and began to unpack the vaccines. The house was packed, and everyone seemed to be talking at the same time.

'They are asking why you do not take off the clothes,' Charlie translated for her. 'I give them an answer already, huh?'

'I—I don't believe it!' she murmured in return. 'Why is it so warm. And why do they take off—why, that woman has taken everything off except that little pair of shorts!'

'Nice, huh?' he answered. 'Is the custom. You do not wish? The heat comes from the many people, and also from all those blubber lamps that never go out. And under that stone bed-platform is a very tiny fire. At least take off your outer jacket.' He helped her slip out of one third of her bulky clothing, her parka.

One of the woman came directly up in front of her, looked closely, and touched. They all burst out laughing. 'She says you can't be real woman,' Charlie interpreted. 'You got no breasts, huh. I tell her you got so much you don't show so not to make them feel ashamed. It is the way with the people. To make laughter.' He sputtered a few more words to the group, and gradually the Inuit women backed away from her.

'Now what?' she queried.

'I tell these people you come directly from Akilinek. That is the land on the other side of the world, where the Inuit come from. I tell them you are favourite slave of the *Tornit*, the ice-giants, and you are so pale because they keep you inside the caves all the time. Except for now. They know it's not true, but they like a good story. You ready?'

After the uproar, the actual immunisation took only a few minutes. She made a careful record, doing her best to keep the inquisitive children out of the way. There were no immediate reactions to the shots. Terry smiled at them all, moved over to the bed platform, and sat down. Immediately the children gathered at her feet, and the women formed a half-circle in front of her. The heat was beginning to affect her. She tugged her way out of her sweaters, and unbuttoned the top buttons of her thermal underwear. The women began to giggle, hiding their mouths behind upheld hands. She turned to Charlie again. He was laughing at her. 'They are embarrassed,' he said. 'They say to apologise. They see you are very much woman, like I said. Now they want to know if you can be white all over. I tell them yes, but they don't believe!'

'And they won't believe me, either,' she snapped at him. 'I'm not running a side-show!' But of course she was. Much later, after a meal of hot stew which she could not identify, the men all left to go to another building. Terry stretched herself out on the community bed, snuggling into the bear-skin allotted to her, and found immediately that it was too hot. Huddled in her assigned corner, in darkness, she tossed and turned, and gradually, one piece at a time, stripped off all her heavy clothing. When she finally lay back to sleep, she was dressed only in her lace-trimmed briefs.

The dream was a wild variation of one that had bothered her for years. She was back in the house on Hawthorne Street where her mother-in-law ruled. She was alone, na-ked, running through the corridors, screaming for Tim. His mother and four replicas were chasing her, screaming in-sults, taunting her for her clumsiness, for the pale olive of her skin, for her stupidities. In her dream they were all car-rying switches, and they swung and snapped them, missing her by inches. And then she fell down, and they were on her, their hands running up and down through all the secret places of her body, and they were laughing at her. The hands woke her up. She was lying on the sleeping platform, with seven women kneeling around her. They were touching her gently, caressing her pale skin, making admiring noises. When she sat up, they fell back silently, watchfully. She knew she had to make an effort to reassure them, but had no words. So instead she smiled at them all, pulled one of the little baby girls over, and cuddled the baby to her breast. Everyone laughed, the tension was released, and another day began.

She had dressed and eaten before Charlie and Major Gorton came in. She was still chewing on a stringy piece of pemmican meat when Charlie squatted down on the floor beside her. He sighed. 'You don't know how lucky you are to be a woman,' he said. 'We hold a *Qagsse*—an assembly of all the men—last night. We talk all night. Not too bad, but I get old. You like it here?'

'It would take some getting used to,' she laughed. 'But look. I've traded my GI trousers for some real skin ones. Look at those splendid colours! And so soft and warm!'

'Yes,' he grunted glumly. 'Very important, clothes. Times like this I think my father is right, huh. Always he says to me, Ungarlak, he says, at thirty summers you should marry! How about that, Terry. You want to marry with me?'

'Oh, come off it, Charlie,' she snorted. 'You know you wouldn't want me. And why are you talking about marriage now?'

'Oh, you are right,' he laughed. 'You are pretty good to look at—for a white girl. But your nose sticks out too far, and you got funny eyes. Not bad, you understand, but funny, huh. Why get married? You can see reasons all around you. Where I live, in the south, man can live in a wooden house and have a woman or not, it makes no difference. But up here, man cannot live without woman; woman cannot live without man. Take the headman, here. He hunts, he fishes—it takes all his days. His woman makes the house, keeps it warm, makes the food. He brings home sealskin. His woman dries it, and then she sits down and chews it. Every inch she chews it—and that's what makes your pants so soft, and warm. He hunts seal to feed her; she chews skin to keep him warm while he hunts. Everything is circle. Up here life is simple, like God intended. Man cannot live without woman; woman cannot live without man. Hey, enough talking. Hear the dogs? Here come the teams!'

She followed him slowly out into the sunshine, her head spinning. Woman cannot live without man. Oh God, she thought, can it really be that simple? They had nothing, these people. Nothing but happiness. The lovely little girl who had lain at her breast, gurgling, then scrambled up to rub noses with her while everyone laughed. Terry could feel an undefinable longing creeping up on her. There was a need, a fulfilment that she required. In the distance she could hear the dogs barking.

'Bad training,' Charlie muttered as he helped her over the rock-strewn path. 'Dogs supposed to run, not bark.'

Her eyes adjusted gradually to the bright sun, and she looked out on to the sea ice where the Inuit was pointing. Two sleds were bouncing over the rough ice, each drawn by its own pack of eight trotting dogs, leashed side by side in the Greenland fashion, rather than one after the other as in the Alaskan and Canadian style. Four men were trotting beside the sleds.

'Runs good for white man, huh?' Charlie grunted.

'How in the world would you know?' Terry queried. She fumbled in the pocket of her parka for her sun-glasses. The four men were hardly more than dots on the ice.

'Two in front, they run standing up,' he commented. 'Wiggle the arms, huh. Keep the head up. Very proud. Maybe fall down very easy. White men. Two in back, they run leaned over. Feet drag a little, like man must run in show-shoes. Keep head down to see where foot goes. Keep sun out of the eyes. Inuit. Easy.'

'Oh! Of course, I see,' she lied. 'Where are they coming from?'

'Is the science people. They come to learn how to live on the ice before they go north. They go out with Inuit. Keep warm in tent. Hunt for food. Fish. Stay alive. Good to know. Maybe some day even manage dog team—but I doubt that. Too much to expect.'

The sleds had reached the edge of the ice. Both teams wrestled up the incline for about twenty yards, and stopped. The dogs collapsed in their traces. The two Inuit began unloading the sleds. The women of the settlement rushed down to do the heavy carrying. The other two men slowly climbed up to the level of the houses, and took off their hoods and face-masks.

'Charlie!' The big man in the lead embraced the Inuit guide in a bear-hug. 'Lousy run,' he continued. 'Seal haven't come north yet. Saw a couple of polar bears itching for a fight, and managed to catch a few fish through the ice. I'm hungry, man!'

'Good to be hungry,' Charlie laughed. 'You too fat. Good for you to be hungry. You meet the nurse? Nice-looking—for a white woman.'

'Yes, I know,' he said. 'Hi, Terry, you waiting for me?'

'Waiting for you! Boy, what a nerve! We came to inoculate the family that's moving south. Why in the world would you think that I was—' She was unable to control the babbling, but Tim could. He wrapped those long arms around her tiny frame and sealed her lips with his.

The arctic cold seemed to accentuate the pleasure. Taken unawares, she struggled only briefly, then lay contentedly in the circle of his arms and savoured the honey of his touch. When he finally put her down, she was too dazed to argue.

'Hey, what I told you,' Charlie chuckled. 'Man cannot live without woman. This your woman, Tim?'

'Yes. This is my woman, Charlie. But she has this problem—she doesn't believe it.'

'Best way take them to bed, I hear it. But the fly-boy is eager to go home, huh? You better hustle.'

Behind them they could hear the engine of the helicopter stutter and stammer in the deep cold, and finally fire. They walked up to the door of the aircraft and climbed in. To the natives in the village it seemed that unloading the sleds and examining the results of the hunt was more important than saying goodbye to the helicopter. Not even the children turned from their task as the machine vaulted into the clear sky.

The cabin grew warmer very quickly, and they all shrugged themselves out of their outer clothes. Charlie and Major Gorton were in the front seats, carrying out some wild arguments which could not be heard. Tucked into the back seat between her husband and the stranger who was the other scientist, Terry did her best to be inconspicuous. It wasn't hard, for the two men seemed to have a thousand things to talk over concerning their trip, and she was so short that they could talk over her head with ease. But there was one difficulty.

As soon as they were strapped in Tim had turned to talk across her, and his left hand casually draped itself over her shoulder, while his right sought and found the warmth of her clasp. The touch electrified her. She peered at him out of the corner of her eye, but could read nothing in his expression. At about five minutes into the flight he recalled his manners.

'Teresa,' he said, 'this is Henry Merryweather, my partner. Henry, this is my wife.'

Just like that! This is my wife! Excuse me, but this package that I have found in the Arctic—this small female package just happens to be my wife! She wondered if she might have the nerve to lift up his hand to her mouth and bite him. She started to move it, and to her surprise found that it was all lightness—or he was helping. But there was a strange lethargy creeping over her, a dazed willingness to surrender all her problems, to disassociate herself from her body, and to let fate happen. When the hand reached the vicinity of her mouth she leaned over slightly and kissed it. He stopped talking just long enough to smile at her, and then went on with the conversation.

The smile was another catalyst. A tingling feeling in her toes spread rapidly throughout her tense body, relaxing it, letting her see with clearer eyes, to perceive with deeper understanding. 'You know what,' she whispered to herself, 'I'm happy!' She leaned just the slightest bit in his direction. He took no notice. She inclined another two inches. His arm shifted around her shoulder and his giant hand pulled her over farther. Without a struggle she collapsed against him letting her head come to rest on his chest with the top of her crown of curls barely reaching his shoulder. She sighed contentedly, closed her eyes, and let their conversation flow over her head like a grateful benediction.

The landing was unexceptional. A storm was evidently expected. Base personnel were scrambling to push the 'Ready' aircraft into the hangars. The chopper swayed a little, bounced once, and squatted within its circular pad. She could see fluff clouds already building up in the north-west quadrant as she crawled and scrabbled her way down the steps of the helicopter. The men followed, with Charlie sharing the weight of her medical bag with Tim. The whipping wind, at such low temperatures, was already making breathing difficult. In the shelter of one corner of the hangar Tim stopped her by putting a hand on her arm.

'We have to leave almost at once, Terry,' he said quietly. 'And we'll be gone for the summer. But you and I have a million more things to talk about. How about coming with me now. We'll go along to the Club for a second breakfast.'

She threw back her hood to get a better look at him. 'I—I have to know something first,' she hedged. 'When your mother—' A flash of disgust swept Tim's craggy face. 'Well, I have to know,' she half shrieked at him. 'Your mother said—she—that you were terribly angry, and wanted to—get your hands on me and—do you?'

He shook his head in disbelief. His eyes sparked, and the hands holding each of her arms squeezed until they hurt. 'Don't tell me you're becoming some kind of stupid,' he grated at her. 'Of course I want to get my hands on you. What the hell do you think?'

It was enough. Enough to destroy all those little dream castles she had been building. All those little sequences that began with 'Tim and I!' They all vanished in the few seconds it took him to make his declaration, leaving her the taste of ashes in her mouth, and the bitter remembrance of six years of fear.

She relaxed all her muscles, and the movement so surprised him that she slipped downwards out of his hold. For a second she scrabbled against the slippery ice underfoot, and then managed to get her feet under her. She barrelled

off around the corner of the hangar towards the road. Her
luck was in, for once. The hospital ambulance was making
a leisurely approach up the incline. She waved it to a stop
and scrambled up into the seat, slamming the door against
his call, and urging the driver to make a U-turn and head
back to the hospital.

She hid in her room for the rest of that day, and all that
night, refusing to answer the various knocks on the door.
The weak sun was almost obliterated by midnight, as the
threatened storm moved in. When she woke up the next
morning the world outside was a grey haze, and the wind
was whistling between the buildings, blowing new snow
across the old drifts.

The storm continued for four days, bringing most activ-
ities on the base to a stand-still. She stifled her agony by
throwing herself into the routine of work. Two separate ac-
cidents brought in four patients, and she wore herself out
providing the highest level of care which none of them really
needed. But at least it got her to sleep. And after the storm
had moved on, and the plough had cleared the streets, she
found further comfort.

The sun had gradually established its way over the north,
and the banks of snow were gradually being turned into
melt-water. For a day or two she marvelled at nature. For as
soon as the sun had removed the snow-cover in any partic-
ular area, that zone turned blue and red and green as thousands of tiny flowers blossomed, sparkled, and seeded in
that frantic life-cycle that the Arctic dictates. And as the
flowers seeded, the giant arctic rabbits that lived on those
plants ventured down from the mountains on to the base,
followed by the tiny blue fox that lived on the rabbits, and
the cycle of life continued.

It was mid-morning, some three weeks after her trip to
Etah, and Terry had showered and dropped into bed after a
midnight-to-morning shift. She drew her double-curtains to
shut out the sun, set her alarm, and dropped off. Just an

hour after her head hit the pillow somebody started to bang on her door. 'All right, all right, come in,' she groaned.

The door opened on the youngest of the male orderlies assigned to the hospital. 'Lieutenant Alden! A Base emergency! They want you right away. Full arctic gear. There's been a bad accident on T-7 and they need a flight nurse, and you're the only one on the Base and Major Malson says for you to get going and she's packing your medical bag and getting the particulars.' He had run out of breath. A nice young man, Terry thought as she fumbled for her robe. He liked to talk when they were on night duty together—all about the little girl he loved in Brownsville, Texas. He disappeared up the corridor, to be replaced by a yawning Ellen, rubbing sleep from her eyes.

'Boy are you lucky,' Ellen commented.

'Yeah! Lucky!' Terry laughed at her. 'Have you ever been in an Inuit village, Ellen?'

'Nope.'

'All the woman wanted to touch me—all over. I began to feel like a package of yard goods. I need a shower if I'm going out like that again.'

'Men too, probably,' Ellen retorted. 'Touch you, I mean. They're the same no matter where you go. Don't forget your soap.'

Terry collected it, and the two women went down the hall together, chattering. Terry stepped up into the shower, and the shock of the cold water woke her up completely. She turned on the warm, and let the water bring her up to normal operating speed. She stuck her head out past the curtain when she had soaped up. 'What is this T-7?' she asked. Ellen walked over and stood just outside the curtain, out of range of the spray.

'It's an island,' she shouted. 'An island made of freshwater ice. There are about ten of them in the Arctic Ocean. In the summertime they drift all the way around the Arctic basin. Right now T-7 is somewhere in the Robeson Channel, at the very northern tip of Greenland. It's frozen in for the winter. The scientists are using it as a station for their instruments.'

'How the devil do I get there? Walk?'

'Fly, of course. It's a big island. A big floating flat-topped aircraft carrier, courtesy of Mother Nature. You'll see when you get there. Do you have all the luck!'

'Yeah, sure. Lucky!' Terry said wryly as she stepped out and dried herself off. 'You should be so lucky. Ever try sleeping on a stone bed-platform? You end up sleeping either flat on your back or on your stomach!' She wrapped her huge bath towel around her sarong-wise and hurried back to her room.

Once again she went through the ritual. Loose thermal underwear over her favourite pair of blue lace briefs. Add one loose sweater. Slip on the sealskin trousers, and fasten them with braces. A light triple-insulated jacket over the suspenders. And then an outer water-proof set of coveralls. All loose. Balloon Annie. 'Can you see me out there?' she called.

'How could I miss,' Ellen returned. 'Now you've got yourself all suited up, how do you suppose you can bend over to put on your mucklucs?'

Terry made a desperate try to bend in the middle, but only managed to fall over on the bed.

'I'll get the damn things,' Ellen laughed. 'Boy, do you really have all the luck!'

'Yeah,' Terry snorted from under her mountain of clothing. 'You could talk me out of it easy. Steer me to the door. Where the devil did I put my fur cap?'

'It's out with your parka. Mush!'

'They don't say "mush" in Greenland!'

'What do they say?'

'I don't know. I didn't get around to asking, but it wasn't "mush". Take me to our leader, lady.'

Jim Callagher was waiting for her, with Mary at his side. 'We don't know how bad things are,' he told her. 'There was a garbled radio message from the ice-island at about three o'clock this morning, and we haven't been able to get back to them since then. The message indicated that one of the men had slipped, or fallen. He may have been up on the radio mast they were putting up, so he might have fallen a good distance. I thought I would go myself, but we have three important operations scheduled here today. Dr Fine isn't up to a trip like this. Anyway, for some screwy reason, the only part of the message we got clearly was " . . . evacuate. Send a plane and a flight nurse." And so there you go!'

'What should I take?'

'The usual general medical bag. I've thrown in a few bags of saline solution. There's bound to be some shock. But remember, your job is to get him strapped into the emergency stretcher, and get him back on the plane. Don't try anything fancy. All we want to do is get him out of there alive.'

'How long a trip is it? I haven't any idea where it is.'

'It's about five hundred miles from here. You'll be using the twin Beechcraft. It should cruise about two hundred miles an hour. So give or take half an hour, it's a three-hour trip. Loading time for the patient I can't estimate. Then they'll have to refuel the plane by hand. That takes another hour. I would guess maybe ten—eleven hours for the round-trip. Not scared are you?'

'I don't know about—oops. I've just remembered what they told us in flight training. They said if you were the only calm and sensible person in a crowd of people running around with their heads cut off, it was most likely because you didn't know what was going on! That's me. Of course I'm scared,' she grinned. 'Lead me to the flightline.'

Having bundled herself up so thoroughly to face an arctic day, Terry suffered the further indignity of making the trip to the flightline in the ambulance, 'because it has a heater, you know.'

In a matter of minutes the ambulance pulled up on the ready line beside a ski-equipped twin engine plane that was obviously looked after with 'executive care'. Terry climbed down from the ambulance and waddled over to the pilot, who was making a careful inspection of the skis.

'I'm the nurse,' she shouted, trying to be heard above the noise of the rising wind. The pilot stood up, turned around, and smiled at her.

'Lieutenant Alden,' he laughed, 'fancy meeting you here!'

'For goodness' sake, Major Gorton,' she replied. 'Do you do *all* the flying at this base? We have to stop meeting like this. People might talk!'

'It's a question of economics,' he shouted back. 'I fly, I get flight pay. I don't fly, I get sympathy. Climb in, Lieutenant. There's no good time to fly to the North Pole, so we needn't wait for something better.'

'Are we really going to the North Pole?' She could not disguise the edge of excitement in her voice.

'Near enough to write home about,' he chuckled. 'Within two hundred and fifty miles. Less if my navigation is poor, and we miss the ice-island.'

'Is that likely to happen?'

'Anything's likely to happen in a land where the north magnetic pole is south of us. How about that? Fasten your safety-belt. Landing and take-off on skis is sometimes exciting.'

CHAPTER FOUR

IT WAS TEN O'CLOCK in the morning when they rolled out to the end of the runway. She watched as the major manipulated the throttles, checked the instruments, and talked to the tower. He seemed a different man, sitting at the controls. He was a man in command, his actions crisp, knowing. She glanced across the mass of dials and knobs in front of them and sighed, wondering how any one man could have mastered it all. Her thoughts must have shown on her face.

'Buckle up,' he laughed. 'I've been doing this for thirty years!' The craft moved out on to the runway, set its wheels on the broad white line painted there, and shook as an engine ran against the brakes. He took one more look around, listened to some instructions on his earphones, and released the brakes.

Within minutes they were airborne, making a lazy turn north of Mount Dundas, and cutting the corner of Smith Sound on their way towards the Kane Basin. He was busy for the first few minutes. Then he flipped two switches, and settled back in his seat. 'We'll go all the way on the water route,' he told her. 'There's a bad storm on the way. A big one. I think we'll get there before it catches up to us, but if we don't, I want us to be away from the ice-cap and those mountains.' He pointed ahead on the left, where the cold jagged peaks of the Victoria and Albert Mountain range split Ellesmere Island in two.

Terry, always inquisitive, tried to make some sense out of what was happening. Most of the instruments were steady, and the aeroplane was forging slowly past the immense mountain range, occasionally dipping and rising. But the major was leaning back in his seat, both hands in his lap, with his eyes closed.

'Major?' She did her best to keep her voice steady, but it was not to be. He opened one eye and smiled at her. 'Isn't— don't you—suppose we hit something?'

'Up here?' His laugh was hearty. 'Not to worry. Look down by your feet. You see those four black boxes?' She lifted her feet, as if something down there might bite her.

'Yes?' she said hesitantly.

'Okay. So the middle box is an inertial guidance computer. It decides where we go. It tells the one on the left. That's the automatic pilot, and it's flying the plane. The one on the top is a transponder. Every two minutes it asks the navigational satellite where we are. The satellite tells him, and he tells the computer. And then the computer tells the autopilot what to do. And the fourth box, it keeps measuring how high we are above anything solid. Simple.'

'Yes, of course!' She drew back in her seat, wondering how many other ways there were to be a fool! Simple. She hadn't the slightest idea what he was talking about. Satellites? Trying not to be conspicuous, she edged over to the window by her seat and looked up.

'You can't see it from here,' he chuckled. 'It's in a stationary orbit 20,000 miles up. And everybody in the northern hemisphere uses it—aircraft, ships, submarines. And maybe even the birds, for all I know.'

She shook her head, laughing at herself. 'Don't be too impressed,' he added. 'Turn me loose in a hospital and I'd kill all the patients within the hour. You have your thing, and I've got mine!'

'I wish I understood one tenth of what's in your head,' she confessed. 'You've a lot of experience in arctic flying?'

'This is my fourth tour up here,' he replied. 'You know how it goes. No family, no dependants—so I might just as well be up here, where a guy my age can still fly. If I were in the States I'd be filling inkwells in the Pentagon, and receiving weekly invitations to retire.'

'You could be pretty comfortable, retired.'

'Sure, but I couldn't fly. It's like a disease. I've been flying since the Korean War. I couldn't give it up if I wanted to. And I don't want to.'

'But it's terribly dangerous!'

'Not as much as you think. Statistically I'm as safe here as I am in the bath tub at home—'

'Which is a pretty dangerous place,' she laughed.

'Which is—' he acknowledged. 'But you know, life offers a whole bunch of choices. I love to fly. And I've concluded it's better to love what you're doing, even if it kills you, than to be safe and unhappy. Look down there!'

He pointed just ahead and down. She could see some movement on the ice below, but the sun was slipping in and out of cloud banks, and it was hard to see.

'Polar bears,' he told her. 'First sign of spring.'

Terry watched for a moment, and then, lulled by the drone of the engines and the interminably slow march of mountains by the window, she became drowsy. She leaned back, checked her seat-belt, and slipped off into a deep sleep. As she drifted away her mind wrestled with words. 'Better to love—even if it kills you. Man must have woman, woman must have man.'

'Yes,' she whispered, 'yes.' And a smile lit up her solemn face, as if she had just made a momentous discovery.

A firm hand shaking her shoulder woke her. 'Teresa? Teresa, wake up!'

'I'm awake,' she said groggily. 'Are we in trouble?' There was just enough light outside for her to see that they were flying between two dark grey layers of clouds. The bottom of the upper layer glowed as the sun struggled to break through. The clouds in both layers were racing past them, moving south-eastwards.

'We've got a small problem,' the pilot told her. 'The storm is massing faster than the Met people had thought. We're going to go down through that lower layer of clouds, and see if we can pick up the beacon on T-7. We're at the upper end of Robeson Channel now. It'll get pretty bumpy. I want you to go to the back end of the aircraft. There's a jump seat back there beside the emergency stretcher.'

'Why?' she asked.

'Don't bug me,' he said. 'Just go. It's safer back there.'

She hesitated, wanting to know more, but the look of concentration on Major Gorton's face caused her to think again. She unsnapped her safety-belt and made her way to the rear of the cabin. Even before she found her new seat the plane began to buck and sway. She settled down, strapped herself in tightly, and looked back at the cockpit. The major was holding up a pair of earphones, and gesturing to her. She looked around and found a similar set beside her seat. She brushed back the hood of her parka and slipped them on over her ears.

'We're under the cloud layer at three thousand feet,' she heard him say. 'According to the satellite that damn island should be right in front of us, give or take five miles. Where the hell is that beacon?' His voice sounded as calm and as cool as if he were on a rocking-chair back in Mississippi.

'My God, look at that!' She could see nothing, and had to wait for him to explain. 'I've got the beacon,' he told her. 'It's almost two points off our flightline! Either the satellite is lying to us, or—'

'Or what?' she prodded.

'Or that damn island is moving! And that can't be. It's too early in the year for it to be drifting. I wish one of those clowns would put on the landing lights. My IFF beacon has been signalling for five minutes. Ahhh! There they go. Look at that!'

By craning her neck Terry was able to see out of the windscreen as the plane went into a deep dive. Directly in front of them, like a great ocean liner stuck in a white sea, a massive island of ice sparkled at them from the light of twenty landing lights. The island stood fifty feet or more above the level of the surrounding sea ice. Off to one side she could see a cluster of buildings, looking almost like a Maltese Cross, half-covered with snow. Three other small building complexes dotted the flat surface, but were unlit. Gusts of wind were slapping across the surface of the ice, creating little whirlwinds of snow.

'Okay now,' Major Gorton said, as if he were talking to himself. 'Everybody's home safe!' She smiled at his obvious relief. She could see the flaps on the wings crank down, and the pitch of the motors changed as they dropped down towards the welcome landing area. And then suddenly, as if some giant hand had wiped the slate, it all disappeared, leaving them wallowing in a cocoon of white.

'Oh my God!' Major Gorton said quietly. 'White-out! Hold on to your hat!' His hand moved towards the throttles, and she could see him jerking them to full power. But the right-hand engine, idling too low, failed to catch. It sputtered, stammered, and stopped. Like a slow-motion segment of a movie, Terry watched as the plane dropped into the cloud of snow, fluttered vainly, and then touched down on something hard and unyielding. For a moment they slid forward, and then the left-hand ski caught against something, snapped, and the fuselage flipped over on its back and continued to slide down the ice runway. The left engine ran itself up as the propeller snapped off, and then went quiet. The body of the aircraft was now sliding sideways. It cracked into something, and split in half. The forward end, bearing the pilot, cart-wheeled forward, while the rear section came to a stop almost immediately.

As quickly as it had come, the white-out disappeared. The lights were still on, and a temporary quiet had descended. It had all happened so quickly that Terry, struggling with the safety-belt that held her to what was now the top of the craft, could not bring her mind to comprehend what had happened. She could look directly out of the hole where the plane had broken up and see the front end, not two hundred feet ahead of her. And as she watched, confused, there was a flicker of light at one of the wings, and then the whole forward section, containing the pilot, the wings and the petrol tanks, burst into a tower of flame.

Terry fumbled with the release button on her belt, aware that some female voice was screaming in her ear, and her fingers finally solved the puzzle. The belt snapped back, releasing her, and letting her fall the five or six feet to the snow-covered ice. She staggered to her feet and made an ineffective move towards the burning wreckage. By now she knew that she was doing the screaming. She stopped, covering her mouth with both gloved hands. At just that moment the burning section of the plane blew up, something crashed into the side of her head, and she pitched into the dark chasms of unconsciousness.

She came back slowly and her first impression was one of warmth. The chill wind had gone, snow no longer nipped at her cheek, and there was the delicious feeling of comfort. She cautiously opened one eye and looked around. She was lying on a bunk-bed in the right hand end of a commercial house-trailer. A fluorescent light cast its white glare across yellow walls and dark ceiling. Just opposite her was a second bunk.

A man lay there, fully dressed, eyes closed. His left hand was restlessly twitching at the rough blanket that half covered him. His breathing was laboured and irregular. Terry opened her other eye experimentally. Her head ached, and with one finger she probed the rising bump behind her left ear. Her hands were scratched in long parallel lines, but all the rest of her seemed to be present and correct. She tried to sit up, felt dizzy, and fell back on to the bed.

A noise drew her attention to the other end of the trailer, some thirty-five feet away. Her eyes glanced by the little shower cubicle and shower facility, into darkness. She heard a door open, and a light flashed on over a kitchen facility. The sudden brightness hurt her eyes and aggravated her headache. Terry closed her eyes as footsteps came towards her, and she felt someone bend over her bed. She could smell the lingering trace of pipe tobacco, and a warm breath caressed her cheek. And then warm lips touched hers in a tender salute. Terry's eyes flew open.

'I'm not going to eat you,' her husband said as she whimpered and tried to slide away from him. Her shoulder began to ache and her eyes widened with fear. But she managed to shift her weight the entire width of the bed, where her hip banged into the cold wall.

'What—what are you doing here?' she asked.

'This is where I work,' he said. His voice was neither warm nor cold. It sounded as if he were trying to sound casual. There was a tiny smile playing around the corners of his full strong lips. His eyes followed her every movement, every facial expression. And then they shifted from her face to where her breasts were heaving against the thin sheet that covered her. Terry's hand explored—everything but her tiny lace-edged briefs had been removed.

She clutched at the sheet which had fallen carelessly around her, and tried to sit up. 'Major Gorton?' she asked.

He shrugged his shoulders in a Gallic gesture which had never seemed out of place with him. 'There was nothing we could do. He must have died instantly.'

'You—you just didn't leave him there for the animals to—'

'We don't have any animals on this island. And no, I didn't leave him there. How do you feel?'

'Dizzy. Weak. I'll be all right. Did you save my medical bags?'

He nodded towards the front end of the trailer. 'Three of them—all safe. I brought in the stretcher, too.' He was about to say something else when the man on the opposite bed groaned. Tim turned towards him, and behind his back Terry managed to squeeze herself out of the bed. A man's worn blue robe lay on the small chair by the side of the bed. She slipped into it, thankful that it reached to her ankles, and went over to the patient.

'Move aside, please,' she said quietly. Tim looked down at her in surprise, and then moved to the foot of the bed.

Terry examined the man carefully. His face was pale grey, with a line of blue around his lips. The lacerations on his head had stopped bleeding. Her fingers dropped to his wrist, and she concentrated as she tried to count his fluctuating pulse. It was rapid, erratic, hard to read. She checked again against the sweep hand of her large-dial wrist-watch.

'Where do you want the bags?' Tim was back at her side with the three medical bags in his hands.

'Put that first one on the bed, here. The others on the floor,' she said.

She found her stethoscope on top of everything in the instrument bag, and held the diaphragm against her own cheek for a few minutes to take the arctic chill off it. Then she slid it under the patient's shirt. She could hear the impatient heart, the rasp of his troubled breathing. 'Get me a knife or something,' she said quietly as she reached into the bag for her blood-pressure kit. 'We have to get his clothes off without moving him too much.'

'Let me do it,' he answered. From a sheath at his belt Tim pulled out a wickedly sharp Bowie knife. Within minutes the patient was stripped. Terry's eyes and hands roamed gently over the man's body. She made careful note of the massive dent in his chest, the lacerations on both legs, and the odd angle of his left arm. The man groaned once, then fell silent. She leaned over and used a thumb to raise each of his eyelids in turn. The pupils were unequal. She stepped back from the bed and thought for a moment.

'I forgot his name,' she said softly.

'Henry. Henry Merryweather,' he answered. 'We've been working together for three years. He was hooking up the radio antenna, and was blown off the tower. He must have fallen twenty-five feet. What do you think?'

She shook her head, and was rewarded by a sharp pain from the region of the bump behind her ear. Her eyes went out of focus for a second. Her hand grabbed at her husband's shoulder until the wave of dizziness passed, and then she gritted her teeth and set her hands to work setting up the saline drip bag.

Terry picked up the patient's right arm, held the hand and wrist up to the light so that she could plot the course of the major artery, then slipped the drip needle in. A few turns of medical tape bound hand and needle to a wooden board, to keep them still. Terry looked around for a place to hang the bag, and found a projecting hook just at the head of the bed. Then she carefully adjusted the clamp at the end of the long plastic tube, and started the liquid to flow.

'We need to immobilise his arm,' she told her husband. 'In that second bag there's an inflatable pressure bag. Can you find it?'

Tim handed the package to her and watched with concern as she stretched her tiny frame over the bed, surrounded the broken arm in the plastic support, and inflated the bag. Perspiration was running down her face, but suddenly there was a towel present, and Tim was using it to dry her forehead. She threw him a quick smile, then frowned down at Merryweather.

'Difficult?' he asked.

'Very difficult. He's got a concussion, at least two broken ribs, a broken arm, and some internal injury. There's not a lot we can do for him here. We have to get him back to the Base.' And me, too, she thought, as the contents of the room went out of focus again. The ache in her head had grown to mammoth proportions. She staggered back from the patient and collapsed on the other bed as her weak knees bumped up against it.

'What is it, Terry?' Tim sat down beside her and slipped a helping arm around her shoulders. With a sigh of relief she collapsed against him.

'It's nothing,' she murmured. 'My head hurts. I need to—'

'You need to rest,' he grated. 'Why don't we just give Henry a shot and put him to sleep. You can look at him when you've had some rest.'

'No! Lord, no!' Terry protested vigorously. Somehow she found the strength to pull herself away from her husband's comforting shoulder.

'We've only got morphine. Giving him a shot when he's breathing so poorly could kill him. Just give me a minute. I—can you find me some aspirin?'

Tim went to look and Terry took advantage of the break to stretch herself out carefully on the bed, and close her eyes. When he returned moments later she was already feeling better. She swallowed the pills, sipped at the glass of water, then lay back down again. She counted up to one hundred, making a conscious effort to control her breathing. And then she quietly swung her feet to the floor and went back to her patient.

'He needs—' She stopped to think for a moment. 'He needs to be elevated—almost to sitting position, if we can. Can we find some more pillows. He needs oxygen, too, but I don't have any with me.'

'We've got some. We have an acetylene welding torch in the shed. The oxygen bottles are separate.'

'Bring it—or them,' she told him. 'I'll improvise a mask for him.'

Two tiring hours later she had done all she could for Merryweather. His arm was immobilised, and the steady drip of the saline solution seemed to be helping. They had managed to raise him to a seventy-degree angle on the bed by using all the available pillows in the station. One of the two oxygen bottles sat on the floor, and a rubber tube ran through an improvised madly bubbling bottle of water up to his face, where a surgical mask had been taped over nose and mouth as a temporary device. She checked his pulse again. It was a little stronger, and not so erratic, but his blood pressure was much too low. The patient was quiet, and his breathing had improved slightly. She stepped back from the low bed, arching her stiff back.

'That's all I can do,' she said. Tim handed her a hot cup of coffee. She sipped at it gratefully and followed him to the front of the trailer. Placing the cup down on the little kitchen table, Terry scrubbed her hands and face in the tiny metal sink set into the counter.

'No smoking in here, you know,' she told him as she dropped into one of the chairs, exhausted.

'Boy, you surely give a lot of orders, Teresa Alden,' he said. It was the first time he had used her full name, and for some reason she loved the sound of it on his lips.

'All nurses do,' she answered primly. 'They teach it in second-year nursing. How to give orders and be a bully. Where did you learn?'

'Ouch!' he chuckled. 'I guess I deserve that, don't I?'

He did, she felt sure, but she had no intention of telling him so. It was hard enough, now that the first stage of shock had passed, to maintain her placid equilibrium with him in the room. She felt like a battleground. On one side there was the impulse to run to him, to squeeze herself into the shelter of his arms, to feel her pulse rising as his hands touched her as no other man had ever done. And then there was the other side, the side that urged her to run while she had the chance, to put as much distance between them as she could. Is it possible, she asked herself, to love someone and fear them at the same time? There was no answer. She flexed her arms to relieve them, and winced as a sharp pain tore through her left shoulder.

Tim took two steps towards her, concerned. 'What is it?' he asked.

'I'm not sure,' she replied, rubbing the shoulder gently. 'I think when I released my seat-belt I fell on my shoulder. Or something like that.' And then, trying to change the subject, 'It's important for us to get Mr Merryweather out of here. Can you call for another evacuation flight?'

He shook his head. 'Not possible,' he said. 'That's what Henry was trying to fix when he fell. We don't have an antenna to—hey, wait a minute! You know what?'

'Who, me? I don't know anything about radios. They scare me.'

'Come off it, Terry. I was watching you back there working on Henry. Nothing scares you—not these days. When I married you you were the most beautiful rabbit in the county!'

She stared at his face, memorising his features. What should I say, she thought. That I've grown up? That I've learned about the hard world? Should I tell him that it wasn't easy, and that I have more scars on my heart than on my hand? Or shall I tell him the truth—that I haven't really changed inside! That I'm still a marshmallow, and only the outside crust has become hard? That I only look placid on the outside because I force myself to it? She shook her head, unable to decide what to tell him, and in the end she told him nothing.

'You *have* changed,' he repeated. 'Very much.'

'Of course I have,' she stabbed at him. 'How could I help it! It's all gone, Tim. What do they say, "Love dies when beauty flies out the window?" Or something like that. It's all gone now.'

'Don't kid yourself,' he returned harshly. 'Sure, all that ethereal, virginal beauty is gone, but that was all kids' stuff. Now you've become a real woman, Teresa Maria—a real woman. And the rabbit seems to have turned into a tiger.'

'I don't know that I like all this comparison with animals,' she demurred, smiling down at the table.

'Okay, okay,' he laughed. 'Next time I'll do it better. But
right now I've got an idea. We need an antenna, and I've got
four reels of insulated wire. I'm going outside to lay it out
on top of the snow. That snow is so dry that it might just
make it work.'

'If you say so,' she quipped. He tickled her with one finger under her chin, and went over to the door. Terry followed, shivering as the temperature dropped quickly. She
was standing in a square chamber built of plywood and
could see the ends of three other trailers, one on each side
of the square, projected into the room. Tim was struggling
into outdoor gear and Terry noticed her own hanging on a
separate set of hooks.

'What we have,' he told her as he struggled, 'is four triple-
insulated trailers. They all butt into this cold chamber to
make one building, in the form of a cross. Those two trailers are for personnel, this one for instruments, and the one
directly across from you is our cold storage food locker. But
you'd better get back inside. We never heat out here—and
you're not wearing a great deal.'

She backed away from him slowly, mesmerised by his
eyes. He followed her until she bumped into the door jamb
and stopped. She brushed her hair back off her face, suddenly conscious that she was only wearing his robe. Suddenly aware that she was all female, and that he was—a
hunter?

'I want to kiss you,' he said softly.

Her hands moved to cover her mouth, and a look of surprise flashed across her mobile face.

'For God's sake,' he muttered, 'I don't intend to rape
you. You're beautiful. You're all woman. I want to kiss you.
What's wrong with that?'

'Nothing,' she mumbled. 'Nothing at all.'

'Then why the hell do you have to look so surprised?'

'You wouldn't believe me if I told you!'

'So try me. Come on, Terry.'

'Well, I *am* surprised,' she returned gently. 'It's the first time you ever asked me, Tim. Always before you took. It's the first time you ever asked me for anything!'

'We've set a lot of firsts today, haven't we,' he said. 'It's the first time you ever gave me orders, too. In fact, it's the first time you ever talked back to me!'

He held his arms open to her, and without another thought she walked into their shelter. As he enclosed her in his trap, she laid her head against the wall of his ribs and sighed. He cupped her chin with two of his fingers and raised her head. Then he bent over and gently touched her lips with his. It felt like the brush of summer wind, the touch of the velvet petals of a rose. And it was over almost before it began. 'I've got to get going,' he reminded her, and pushed her away.

Terry leaned back against the door as he walked over to a corner of the cold room and started to climb the cleated ladder nailed against its side. 'What in the world are you doing?' she asked.

'This is the way out, lady,' he laughed. 'The snow gets so deep around here that we put all the entrances in the roof. Would you mind passing me up those rolls of wire?'

She complied, forgetting the nip of the cold in her eagerness to help. He was all the way up to the top now, shining his flashlight on a pair of instruments stuck on the wall against the ceiling.

'Temperature's rising,' he called down to her. 'It was twenty below three hours ago, and it's almost up to zero now!'

'Heat wave?' Terry asked, trying to keep her voice light.

'Heat wave hell!' he snorted. 'Storm. It always warms up around these parts before the winds come. And from the speed of the change I'd say we're in for a big blow. You'd better get back in the warm before I open this hatch.'

She waved one hand in acknowledgement, and hurried back inside the trailer. The warm air hit her in the face almost like a physical blow. She snatched one sip from her coffee cup, then went back to check her patient.

He was still unconscious, breathing a little easier with the oxygen flowing into his lungs. But his face was as white as the sheet on the bed and his pulse was still erratic and weak. She propped him up a little higher, and resettled his broken arm. The IV was dripping steadily, the oxygen hissed gently, and there was nothing else she could do. With all her education, all her experience, there was nothing else she could do. She blinked away a small tear, hearing in the back of her mind the warm voice of Sister Marie, who had taught a course called 'Death and Dying' during her final year at Massachusetts General. 'When you have done everything in your power,' the Sister had taught, 'you must leave your patient in the hands of God.'

She tugged her robe a little tighter around her, and dragged a chair from the front of the trailer to the back. She tried it in three places before finding the right angle. Then she sat down, pushed the chair back to balance on its two hind legs, and put her feet up on the injured man's bunk. She knew she had to stay awake. Although there was little she could do for Merryweather, she had to be ready. In any case, with Tim out in the full force of the storm, she dared not be asleep if he needed help. And she knew from past years of experience that if she drifted off while sitting in this position, the chair would surely fall over and wake her up!

Her eyes committed the first treason. No sooner was she settled than her eyelids became too heavy to hold open. She forced them back up, but could only sustain them for a minute or two. 'Oh well,' she sighed, and let them close. The long day was catching up with her. She had been out at the Club with Ellen and Jim the night before, and then had gone out on duty in the ward at midnight. Only after coming off duty had she been alerted for the emergency flight. She had dozed on the flight for perhaps two or three hours. But two or three hours was not enough sleep for her, and now her body was demanding compensation. She fought off sleep by thinking 'nice thoughts'—which meant, as always, thoughts about Tim.

Why had he married her? Was it just—just because she was beautiful, or sexy? She nodded in disgust. Most girls of South European extraction matured early. And faded quickly. And then what was left? She could not suppress a giggle. Her left hand, without command, was soothingly stroking her flank, from hip to breast—'And there's plenty left!' she told herself amid the giggles.

Her patient snorted. She opened one eye, but could see no important change. She closed the eye again, and went back to her dreams.

And why did *you* marry him? He was—handsome? Lord, he was more than that. He was beautiful! He looked and acted like a young Greek god. Adonis? And was that why you married him, you fool? Or was it more than that? When you were close to him, folded into him, there was the warmth and security, the feeling of being protected against anything. So you married him for security? Or maybe that's what love is! It seemed futile to argue with herself. She couldn't win on either side of the argument! She shook her eyes open, set the chair back on four legs, and peered at her patient.

'And is that what love is, Henry?' she asked. He made no response. 'Is it enough to be secure and protected, and worship him like a slave?' Henry Merryweather bubbled a bit of froth, and paid her no attention. She rubbed her tired chin with her hands, and ran her fingers through her hair again. 'And maybe that's why you were always a rabbit,' she told herself. 'Between Tim and his mother, you had no room to grow! And that's what places you where you are now. An eighteen-year-old kid in a twenty-four-year-old body!'

Terry pushed her chair back on its two legs again, and settled her feet. As her eyes struggled to close an inner voice whispered at her, 'Isn't it nice to be able to blame your faults on someone else?' Half asleep, teetering on the edge of falling over, she grumbled, 'Aw, shut up!' and drifted away.

She woke up the hard way. The chair slipped, thudded down on its four legs, and tumbled her off on to the floor. But there had been another thud, she remembered. Slowly she gathered herself together, checked her patient, and walked the length of the trailer to the door. Fresh swirls of snow were settling on the board floor of the cold room. Through the thin wooden walls she could hear the wind whistling and probing. A snow-covered parka was swinging gently on a hook on the wall. And then she heard another sound. Somewhere her husband was talking to somebody.

She looked back at Merryweather and decided that he might be neglected for a moment. She closed the door behind her, and slipped into her own parka. His voice was coming from the adjacent trailer. She hurried over, opened the door, and stepped in. The entire wall of this trailer was stacked with instruments.

Tim was seated at a little curved table in the middle of the trailer, with a headset over his ears. Two of his fingers were gently rotating the tuning knob on a radio receiver.

Lord, what am I doing, she asked herself. I'm walking in a fog. I'm standing here, watching his fingers, wondering if they will ever soothe me again. If they'll ever run up and down my back and touch that sensitive spot just above my hip. I'm standing here falling in love all over again. He's not a god any more. I don't worship him—but I do love him! I'm making a fool of myself. He doesn't need me. He—please God, help me!

Tim's hand had jumped from the dial to the switch on the microphone. 'Thule Airways Control,' he said into the microphone. 'This is sub-base T-7. Do you read me?' His fingers dropped from the microphone switch and he listened, concentrating. At the same time she must have made some movement, and he saw her out of the corner of his eye. He unplugged the headset from the receiver, and she could hear the answer coming back weakly.

'T-7, T-7,' the disembodied voice said. 'This is Thule Airways Control. I read you weak but understandable. Go ahead.'

He picked up the microphone again, made an okay sign to her with thumb and forefinger, and then made a concise report of conditions on the island.

'Acknowledged, T-7,' the voice answered back to them. 'Understand you request emergency ambulance flight. First evacuation flight has crashed. Nurse is okay, but pilot dead. What is report on first patient?'

Tim passed the microphone to her. Nervously she fumbled at the switch, until his hand closed over hers and guided her. Her voice strengthened as she talked. 'Patient is subject of twenty-five-foot fall. Arm broken, immobilised. Concussion. Surface head wounds, minor. Probably two broken ribs. Internal injuries, and internal bleeding through mouth. Administering saline solution and oxygen. Vital signs poor. Blood pressure now 70/50. Urgently requires evacuation. Urgently!'

There was a pause, then the voice returned. 'Understood, T-7,' the operator said. 'Medical officer here confirms nothing more you can do. Request you keep watch on this frequency in two hours, repeat, two hours, for further instructions. Thule Airways Control out.'

'Well,' he said admiringly. 'Well!'

'Well what?' she asked curiously.

'You did well,' he answered. 'Come on. Let's get something to eat before all hell breaks loose around here.'

'What? You mean the storm?'

'I mean the storm. Look at the barometer.' She looked where he was pointing, but could make no sense out of the instrument. 'It's dropping,' he explained. 'The bottom's falling out of things. Come on.'

He led her back to the trailer where Merryweather lay. She checked her patient one more time, but found no change. Tim had stopped in the fore-section of the unit, and Terry joined him there. 'There's a propane gas stove for cooking,' he told her. 'How would you feel about steak and some vegetables?

'I don't mind,' she said wearily. 'Am I to cook it?'

'Nope. You're the nurse. I'm the housekeeper.' He swung open the door to the tiny enamelled cold-box and pulled out two huge steaks. 'Although I'm glad you're satisfied with steak, since that's the only thing unfrozen at the moment.'

Tim set to work at the tiny stove, while Terry paced back and forth, seemingly exploring, but really watching him out of the corner of her eye. Cook the dinner? In all the year they had been married he had never lifted a finger in the house—and now he was cooking her dinner! She wondered if his mother knew? The thought sobered her. 'Why you didn't even—' she started to say impulsively, then crammed her fist into her mouth to cut off the words.

'Didn't even what?' he asked. He was spreading a light coat of butter over the steak. 'Didn't even what?' he repeated.

'Oh—nothing,' she gasped.

'Come on, Terry, didn't even what?'

'I was just astonished,' she confessed in a small voice. 'When we lived with your mother I don't think you even knew where the kitchen was. I'm sorry, Tim. I shouldn't have thought that!'

'Don't be sorry,' he laughed. 'You're almost right. I knew where it was. That's where the cookie jar was. But I never ever did anything in the kitchen. Neither did my mother!' He turned off the gas, and spooned mixed vegetables on to the two plates. Then he transferred the steaks from the grill to the plate, and set them both on the table. 'That's why I liked coming to your house,' he laughed. 'Your mother is some kind of wonderful woman. Sit down there and dig in. How is your mother these days?'

She slumped into the chair and stared at him. Her eyes were wide, and suddenly tears were forming in the corners. 'Your mother?' Tim prompted as he cut into his steak.

She folded her hands in front of her, elbows on the table. 'My mother is dead, Timmy,' she whispered. 'And Papa and Joao and Fernando. Jimmy and me—we're all that's left.'

He stopped chewing in mid-bite, and used a sip of water to wash it all down. One of his hands snaked across the table and took hers. 'What happened,' he asked.

'It happened four years ago,' she told him. 'Papa needed more money—for the doctors, you know. So he took his boat, the *Three Sisters*, you remember, and he made an extra trip to the Grand Banks just before Christmas. Joao and Fernando went along with him to crew. And they never came back. Three boats were lost at sea in that storm. The news killed Mama. And Jimmy went off in the service.'

'So that explains it,' he said. 'I always thought you would go home to your family. I couldn't see why you would keep running, when you had all that wonderful family!'

'Yes,' she said quietly. 'In one month we lost them all. I had to run. I couldn't stand up under it all. They all thought a lot of you, Tim.'

'And I of them,' he confessed. 'Your father was a great man. You know, it was always my fantasy that if you wouldn't marry me I'd get your parents to adopt me! But that was yesterday. Come on now, eat something. We both need to build up our strength.'

And what surprised her was that she did. She managed to clean her plate, and after the steak was all gone she was amazed. She had not eaten like that in years—or so it seemed.

'That's what you needed,' he said as he stood up and grabbed the dishes. 'There's a lot of you, but it's almost skin and bones compared to what it used to be. You haven't been taking care of yourself. And look at that damn hand.' Tim sat down again, took her left hand in his, and turned it over, exposing all the scars. She pulled back with all her strength, but could not break free.

'Honestly, I never knew,' he said softly. 'Is that why you left me?' She struggled against his hold, trying at least to turn her hand over so that the scars would not be visible. 'Tell me, Terry. I have a legal interest, if nothing else.'

'I'm not your property any more,' she said coldly. 'I'm not anybody's property any more!'

'I don't say you are,' he retorted. 'But you have to believe me. I didn't know!'

She shuddered. 'Yes, I—yes,' she stammered. 'I can believe that you didn't know, Tim. Time was too disarranged. Maybe I fainted twice. I don't know. But I do believe you.'

'Then tell me the rest of what happened. I know now it must have been a tremendous shock to make you run off like that.'

'Don't kid yourself,' she said bitterly. 'I was just a kid. It didn't take a world-shaking event to set me off. They took me to Silvermore hospital. The emergency room was crowded, and they didn't have an empty bed in the place. So they splinted my fingers, gave me a bottle of pain-killers, and sent me back home. The same day, mind you. I couldn't argue with them. I didn't have the guts.'

'And then the next day I got a call from the bank. We were overdrawn. You had been travelling so much that you forgot to deposit your last three pay-packets.'

'Oh my God,' he groaned. His heavy fist thumped the table. 'Every time you say something you indict me further!'

'Don't blame yourself, Tim. It wasn't all your fault. I gave up to panic. I borrowed fifty-five dollars from the next-door neighbours, bought a bus ticket and two boxes of crackers, and went home to Papa. Just a kid trick. And Papa put me back in the hospital. It took almost a year for the operations. And then your mother found me. And you know the rest.'

'I don't know anything,' he retorted angrily.

'Hush, Tim,' she quieted him by putting a finger across his lips. 'Be honest with me. Suppose I hadn't run away? You've become a leader in your field, an adventurer, a man who knows the world. And I would have still been that crazy introverted kid. The kind of wife you would want to hide away somewhere, maybe with a bottle. You know there were hundreds of wives like that in NASA. They couldn't grow when their husbands did. I would have been like that.'

'I—I don't know, Teresa,' he sighed.

'But I do. And now I've got to check my patient. And you'd better go and keep that schedule.'

He nodded agreement and started out to the other trailer. Terry walked part of the way back to the sickbay, but stopped after a few feet and leaned against the wall, clutching at her stomach, trying to hold herself under control. Pray that Air Rescue comes quickly, she told herself. If I have to stay with him here much longer, he—I—It's me I'm afraid of. Not what he'll do, but what I'll do! She stuffed a fist to each eye to keep from crying, and went to see to her patient.

Immediately Terry could feel a difference. His breathing was harsh, slow. Her practised eye measured the drip of the saline solution, and the flow of oxygen from the bottle. She reached for his pulse, and he sighed, a deep rattling sigh.

Twenty minutes later she let herself out of the hospital trailer and went across to the instrument room. As she had expected, Tim was there at the table, already in contact with Thule. A long weather analysis was coming out of the speaker.

'At this time Thule Base is closed to all flights,' the voice was congenial, as if the speaker enjoyed the situation. 'An

Air Rescue plane is standing by at Goose Bay. Met fore-
casts say that the storm may be of two-day duration, or
longer. As soon as weather clears, rescue operations can
begin. Over.'

'Thule Airways, this is T-7. I don't think we can wait. We
have a dangerously injured patient who must be moved.
Can't you do anything tonight or tomorrow?'

The airbase operator began his long-winded explanation
again. She could see that Tim was losing his temper. She
touched him gently on the shoulder, and he looked up. 'It
doesn't matter,' she told him softly. 'We have all the time in
the world. Mr Merryweather is dead.' Tim turned back to
the radio like a wooden statue, and acknowledged the last
transmission.

'I'm terribly sorry, Tim,' she told him. 'I wanted so much
to save him—because he was your friend.'

Tim stood up and put his arms around her. His hands
moved up to the nape of her neck, and rubbed at the tension muscles which always bothered her. A drop of water fell
on her nose, and ran down her cheek. She leaned slightly
back and looked up. Her husband was crying! That strong,
arrogant man, who had let no one else touch his life, was
crying!

'Are you crying for Henry?' she asked softly, lovingly.

'Yes. We're not Spartan warriors any more. He was a
good friend. I'm crying for him—and for us, Teresa. For all
the wasted years, and what might have been.'

She made no attempt to understand. Acting purely on
instinct, she pulled a crumpled tissue out of her pocket,
stretched up on tiptoes, and gently wiped the tears from his
eyes.

CHAPTER FIVE

IT WAS WHILE he was holding her that the cumulative experiences of the day began to catch up on Terry. Her head began to ache. She could feel the pounding pulsations around the bump behind her ear, and her head began to spin. She fumbled for words to comfort her husband, but they would not come. The moment passed, and she slumped in his arms, a large rag doll, with neither muscle nor bone to hold her up. With infinite care he slipped his right arm under her knees and cradled her, his lips buried deep in the wild riot of her soft hair. She sighed in whatever dream that held her.

The wind had risen even higher as he walked to the fourth of the trailers, kicked the door open, and dropped her gently on one of the four bunk-beds that lined its sides. She sighed again, then rolled on her side in a tight little bundle, a smile on her face. He covered her with a blanket and went across the trailer to where Henry Merryweather lay.

All evidence of the medical treatment had been removed. His arms and legs had been straightened, and his hands crossed on his chest. Intermingled with his fingers he could see the glint of gold, the little crucifix which Terry had taken from her own neck and left in his hands. He stood at the bunk-side for a moment, unable to make his last goodbye. And then words came to his mind, Shakespeare's words. 'So may he rest,' he said quietly, 'his faults lie gently on him.'

With a minimum of movement that bespoke long practice he emptied the trailer of his own clothing and the few oddments of food, the books that he had studied nightly, and all the medical materials. At his last act of faith he turned off the heater, cracked open the pipe-ventilator and let in the arctic air, and went out. As he closed the door behind him, he locked it. The little dial thermometer in the door plummeted towards the zero of the arctic night.

Terry was still asleep when he returned, a restless, muttering sleep. Through the mumbling discord of her words he heard a name repeated over and over, but was unable to grasp it. Working carefully so as not to wake her, he loosened the robe, and removed both it and her tiny briefs. He held the tiny garment up to the light, and a smile of remembrance played across his solemn face. When he had removed everything he fetched one of his own soft flannel shirts for use as a nightgown. Before he put it on her he stared at the tiny bundle of feminine mystique that still had the power to sway him. He traced one finger slowly upwards from her tiny toes and ankles, to the fullness of her legs and thighs, to her flat stomach. His eyes widened in surprise as he noted the dull red marks that ran in lines down to her lower abdomen. And then his finger traced upward across her soft full breasts, her swan neck, and her too-thin cheeks.

'My shoulder hurts.' The words broke through clearly. Gently he rolled her over. A huge bruise marked her left shoulder. It started at the collar-bone and went halfway down her back. He went to the kitchen for a bottle of lotion, and carefully smoothed it over the damaged skin. Then he wrapped a towel around a hot packet, and applied it to the area. She stirred slightly when he put it on, but then snuggled herself face-down into the blankets again. He pulled up a chair and lit his pipe, all without taking his eyes from her. When his pipe went cold he removed the hot-pack, slipped the soft flannel shirt on to her, and turned her over.

Almost as if it hurt to do so, he buttoned the shirt, dropping a kiss on each of her dusky-bronze nipples as he covered them up. Then he worked the sheet loose from under her, and placed it over her. As he folded her arms on top of the blanket and buttoned the shirt sleeves, his fingers wandered to her battered left hand. Almost compelled, he stroked the wedding ring that united them—or divided them. He dropped a trace of a kiss on her cheek, and another on her lips. Before he could withdraw, both her hands snaked up around his neck and pulled him down. Barely audible, he heard her say 'Tim! Tim! Thank God you've come home, Tim!' He knelt down by the bed, resting his head against hers on the pillow, until she became quiet again. And then he moved to the bunk across the aisle and threw himself wearily down on it, without bothering to undress.

When Terry woke up the trailer was in darkness. She swung her feet to the floor, fumbling for the slippers that were not there. Her fingers found the lamp switch and twisted it on. The tiny chronometer on the wall was marked out for a twenty-four-hour day, and registered ten o'clock. She tried to force her mind to work. Ten o'clock. In the morning, of course. She had slept the stormy night through. She looked down and noticed that her knees were bare. She clutched at the throat of her garment, recognising it for what it was. She was alone in the trailer.

Hesitantly, she put both feet on the cold linoleum of the floor and padded towards the enclosed cabinet at the middle of the trailer, between the two sets of bunks. She opened the door to find a small wash basin and a chemical toilet. Quickly she splashed her face and tended to her needs. Her clothes, grimy and smoke-coloured, were scattered on two chairs. She picked them up, then dropped them again. Beneath the bunks were a series of drawers. She opened the top one, and found it crammed with men's clothing. She sorted through the lot, picking out a pair of slacks, some heavy socks, and two neckties.

Terry used the neckties for a belt, strapping the trousers around her tiny waist. Then she slipped on the heavy socks, brushed her fingers through her hair, and went looking.

She found Tim in the radio trailer, going down the long row of chattering instruments and recording something on the forms on the clipboard he was carrying. When he heard the door open he looked up.

'Good morning, Teresa,' he said. There was a welcome lilt in his voice.

'Good morning,' she said softly, unable to keep her eyes on his. The trailer was rocking gently, and she could hear the banshee wail of the wind outside. She hugged herself and shivered.

'Look at this.' He pointed down to the moving pens of the instrument in front of him. The pens had just inked their wavery trail off the top of the paper. 'The anemometer has jumped off the scale,' he explained. 'I think the wind has blown the sensors off the roof. The last reading was a hundred and twelve knots.'

'Is that unusual?' She moved closer to him for comfort. He felt her impulsive need, and dropped one arm casually across her shoulders.

'It's happened before, not often. But never in a storm that's lasted this long. I think we're in for a madcap day.'

'Did you ask the man at Thule?'

'Can't raise them. Too much static. The last thing I heard was a broadcast warning of a Force Ten gale. I think the whole Arctic is closed down.'

'Then I suppose we won't see a rescue flight today?'

'Not hardly! I think—' Whatever it was he thought was cut off. The trailer under their feet gave a tremendous jerk, swayed back and forth, seemed to move of its own volition, and then steadied. The shock of the tremor had thrown her against him. She clung, too frightened to breathe.

'Damn it,' he muttered into her hair. 'It can't be. It just can't be!'

'Don't tell me,' she half sobbed. 'I don't want to know!' She burrowed her head into his shirt front.

'It's almost impossible, and you'd better know,' he laughed wryly. 'It's much too early in the year, but the island has broken loose from the ice-pack. We're moving!'

She sniffed a couple of times, and managed to stem the tears. 'Oh, is that all?' she asked coolly.

'Yes, that's all,' he smiled. 'Our ship is afloat, somehow or another. It's probably because this island stands above the ocean ice by a good forty or fifty feet. When a wind of this magnitude hits the side of the island it's just like adding sails. We've broken loose. God knows where we'll go now. I took a look outside an hour ago, and couldn't even see as far as the power building.'

'So what do we do now?'

'Nothing. We couldn't start the island moving, and we can't stop it. We can't steer it, and we can't control it. So the only thing we can do is lie back and enjoy it—as best we can. Let's get some breakfast!'

'Tim, let me make it? You have your work to do here. I don't have anything to do. I'd like to—I want to—it would relieve my mind if I were a little domesticated.'

'Like old times, Terry?'

'No. The old times are gone, Tim.' Her voice sounded wistful. 'They'll never come back. All the wishing in the world won't help.'

'Never is a long time, Teresa. It's not Humpty Dumpty we're concerned with.'

'Isn't it?' She could not stay and talk in that vein. Hurriedly she walked away from him, back to the kitchen of their sleeping trailer. There were eggs in the cold-box. Eggs, bacon, and a half-frozen package of Mrs Gilbert's Brown and Serve rolls. She lit the propane stove, stuffed the rolls into the tiny oven, and began to whip up the eggs for scrambling. It took her longer to find the coffee pot. 'Men!'

she snorted, when she stumbled on it tucked beneath the stove among a handful of cleaning rags.

She watched the bacon crisp in the frying pan. Lord, how much she remembered! He liked his bacon brown and crisp, so that it snapped in his fingers. The high and mighty Aldens, eating bacon with his fingers! He liked his scrambled eggs soft, and his coffee black. She set it all out on the swing-down table next to the stove. It was all ready when he came in.

'Temperature's still rising, barometer's still falling,' he commented. 'Ah. Scrambled eggs. My favourite breakfast. Did you bake these biscuits yourself?'

'Oh yes. Me and Mrs Gilbert!'

'You were always good in the kitchen, Terry.'

'You've got a terrible memory. I couldn't even boil water in those days. You always used to complain because I couldn't even cook a TV dinner. So I took a course.'

'You took a cooking course?'

'Yes. Six months ago.'

'Why, Teresa? Was there some man you wanted to please?'

'I—there hasn't been any other man, Tim. No, I looked in my crystal ball and saw years and years of cooking for myself, and decided that I didn't want to poison myself. I'm pretty good at it, even if I say so myself. You should taste my pigeon breast with lobster sauce.'

'Great day! I stand in awe. Six months ago, huh?'

'Yes.' He was staring at her across the tiny table, as if he were trying to read her mind.

'Was that about the same time you decided to apply for duty in Greenland?'

'I suppose it was, but they were not necessarily connected. What are you trying to read into it?'

'You want it straight?'

'I don't remember you ever sugar-coating anything before.'

'Yeah, well, I wasn't the smartest kid to come down the pike in those days. I have a funny feeling about all this. I've been trying to trace you for years, and then all of a sudden, here you are!'

'Your mother knew where I was. At least those first three years, she did. She knew I was in the hospital, and she knew I went to Massachusetts General Hospital to study nursing. She knew all that.'

'Maybe she did, but she never told me. Until you graduated from the School of Nursing, that is. Then she cut the class picture out of the paper and sent it to me. Just before she died.'

'Why did she hate me, Tim? Why?'

'You have to believe me, Terry. I didn't know that she hated you until we talked, you and I, that first night at Thule. Then you told me something, and it all fell into place.'

'Please tell me?'

'Well, to understand my mother you have to understand pride. She had it. She was an Alden, the reigning queen of Bristol County society. Can you understand that?'

'Oh, I knew that—almost from the first. Being the mistress of the Alden family was more important than anything else in the world to her.'

'You've got it. Even more important than me. Now, there's something else. When my mother was growing up, the Portuguese immigrants were a tiny segment of the population, and everybody looked down at them. In your generation, when more than sixty-five per cent of the people in New Bedford are Portuguese, it's something to be proud of. My mother lived for her position in society. And you threatened her.'

'Me? How could I threaten her?'

'Think, Teresa. My mother wasn't born an Alden. She married the name. Just like you did.'

'I still don't understand, Tim. How could I threaten her?'

'Because my mother's maiden name was Souza.'

'Souza? You mean she was a Portuguese, too?'

'You hit it. But she was Portuguese from the older generation. She was ashamed of it. She hid it very successfully for thirty years. And then you appeared on the scene. You were not only Portuguese, but proud of it. Can't you see? You were willing to boast about being an immigrant—and she had something to hide.'

'But even if I had found out I wouldn't have told anyone.'

'It wasn't the case of "if *you* found out". What she was afraid of was that you, being so blatantly Portuguese, would start all the other old biddies snooping around. And if *they* found out she was a Souza, her whole world would have collapsed.'

'My lord, Tim. And you think that's why she tortured and humiliated me? Just for that?'

'It was her whole life, Terry. She dared not take a chance. Look how she died. Breast cancer. That's the sort of disease that Aldens just don't get—it's too common. So she ignored it, and it killed her.'

'I can't—I just can't understand. She made life miserable, not only for me, but for herself, too, and just for pride?'

He pulled one of her hands away from her face and held it gently. 'I never did know what she was doing, and she never told me anything. For whatever she did to you, all I can say is that I'm sorry. Can you believe that?'

She sniffled and wiggled her fingers free. 'I—I believe you, Tim. But it doesn't make any difference. Not now. Not after all these years.'

'Why don't you tell me about them—all those years?'

'No, I can't do that. Let the dead bury the dead. I've closed off all that part of my life. It didn't happen—she didn't exist.'

'And me? You've closed me off, too? I don't exist?'

'I can't—I—I don't know. Don't ask me, please. There are too many agonies separating us. Drink your coffee—it's getting cold.'

'Yes,' Tim said bleakly. He dropped her hand, drained his cup, and walked out. Ten minutes later, when she peeked around the corner of the door, he was back in the radio room, trying vainly to tune into some outside radio station, looking for help or for news. She fled back to the kitchen.

Woman's work, she told herself as she picked up the dishes and tried to scrub them clean. I'm almost at the North Pole and I'm doing woman's work! Around the world with Teresa Alden. Kitchens I have known and loved! But keeping her hands busy was one way to keep her mind from probing. She finished the kitchen chores, looked over the meagre supply of canned vegetables, and rescued a frozen leg of lamb from the cold-box. So much for dinner. Lunch must take care of itself.

She wandered back to her bunk, picked up all the clothes, his included, and made the place as tidy as she could. There was no broom or vacuum cleaner to be seen, and the floor was rocking beneath her feet. She plumped herself down on Tim's bunk and leaned back.

Be more careful what you say, she admonished herself. He's too sharp—he had made the connection. For years she had known he was looking for her. Twice she had ducked out of jobs barely hours before his detectives notified him. And yet on her applications for duty at Thule she had recorded his name and address. She needn't have done that. She knew it, and obviously he knew it, too. So, why had she done it? She had wanted to go to the end of the world. And she had wanted him to know it! Ball in your court, man! If he had wanted her, he would come, for whatever reason. And he had come. But why had she given the game away? She knew, deep down in her heart—the rabbit was tired of running. And wasn't that a crazy idea! The rabbit wanted the hunter to catch her. Like Major Gorton, she was turning back to the only reality in her life, and if it killed her, she would die happy. That is if she had the guts to go through with it. And as of now it appeared that she did not have the courage.

And what did he want? Both times when she had mentioned that their relationship was buried, he had agreed. As coldly and cleanly as a razor-cut, he had agreed. Which left—nothing. She shrugged her shoulders, and went back to the kitchen.

Lunch was another cup of coffee, and a chocolate bar. 'For energy,' Tim told her.

'What the devil do we need energy for?' Terry enquired.

'I don't know. I just said that. We're still moving—the wind is driving us south-east towards the coast of Greenland. Nyboesland, to be exact. The island drifted east all last year on the ocean currents. When we were first frozen in we were off the tip of Cape Sheridan, and the top of Ellesmere Island.'

'That's why the major couldn't find you! When he made his approach using the satellite, you were something or other off from where you should have been.'

'Don't worry about it. It's still winter. As soon as the wind stops we'll settle down and be frozen in again. Give it another two days, say. Once this island gets moving, it has tremendous kinetic energy. It will take a lot to stop it. Just think of it as a winter cruise on a very large ocean liner.'

'Yeah. Sure,' she agreed glumly. 'An ocean liner. Like the *Titanic*! What do you plan to do this afternoon?'

'I've got another round of instrument readings to record. Then I thought I might try to pick up somebody on the radio.'

'Can I help you?'

'What? Tired of housekeeping already?'

'There doesn't seem to be all that much to do. I thought I might make lamb and baked potatoes for supper. Would that do?'

'Be a change. But you don't have to, you know.'

'I know I don't have to. That's why I'm doing it.'

'Well, if that's—' The lights flickered, flared, and went out. 'Oh brother!' he exclaimed.

'Is that—is it bad?' she asked.

'Hard to tell. The generators have cut out. I'll have to get over to the generator building when the wind dies down.'

'So what do we do in the mean time?'

'Under that second shelf behind you there are a couple of Coleman lanterns. See if you can locate them.'

'I've got one.'

'Pass it over. I'll pump it up and we'll be able to find the rest of the stuff.' She could hear him banging the little air pump against the frame of the lantern to build up the pressure. Then a match flared, dipped, and was instantly replaced by the white glare of the lantern. He set it down on the table while she searched through the cabinet and found two more.

'Save them for emergency,' he told her.

'This isn't an emergency?'

'No, of course not. We have light. We can cook with the propane stove. We have heat from the fuel barrel. All in all we're in good shape, except that all the instruments are out of action. We'll be collecting no more data during this storm. And that's what I'm here for.'

'I see. It's good to know that my safety ranks right up there in second place—behind your instrument data!'

'I didn't mean it that way, Terry, and you know it. Look on the bright side. Instead of recording data, I'll be able to sit and talk with you.'

'I don't—I haven't anything to talk about. I think I'll go and lie down.' She started for the door, but he grabbed her with both hands and forced her back into the chair.

'We *are* going to sit and talk, Teresa!'

'And if I won't?'

'I'm a hell of a lot bigger than you are. Do what you're told.'

'That's still the way it is with you, isn't it,' she flared at him. 'Always the muscles, always the compulsions. Oh, sometimes I wish I were big enough to—to hit you back!'

'To hit me back? What does that mean? When did I ever hit you? When!'

'It—I didn't mean it was always physical. Although there were plenty of times when you bruised me up. You know that. It was the general way you treated me, especially when we were in Houston.'

'I haven't the slightest idea what you're talking about. Lay it out on the table.'

'Yes. If that's what you want.' She swallowed hard and tried to slow her rapid breathing. 'Just for an example, you remember the last time you came home?' She started out slowly, picking her way through a field of memories. 'I went to the airport to get you. I knew you were still mad about my—about the drinking—and I was scared. So damn scared.'

'Of me? That's silly.'

'Of you. I've always been—frightened of you. Even when I loved you the most. Always.' He shook his head in disbelief.

'There was something terribly important that I wanted to talk to you about,' she continued, 'but you flared up right away, and wouldn't speak to me, even after we got home and went to bed. And then you grabbed me in the middle of the night and used me—'

'I don't remember that you fought against it.'

'No. I never did. I'm not accusing you of forcing me, Tim. I enjoyed it. You were a wonderful lover. But it was all lust—not love. I think that's all we ever had going for us. And that's all you ever did. You got home at midnight, had a nap, took me, and went back to sleep. And in the morning you got up and left. I—it was always that way. I had the feeling in the back of my mind that I ought to put a cash register at the foot of the stairs. Yes, I enjoyed it, Tim, but it was more like a series of one-night stands than a marriage! How is that possible? I was a respectably married woman, and you made me feel like a whore!'

'And why the hell didn't you tell me!'

'Me, tell you? Me, tell the master? Why, I didn't even have the guts in those days to choose my own underwear!'

'All right, all right. So things weren't perfect. Is it all my fault?'

'Ah no, Tim.' She leaned across the table and took one of his hands between both of hers. Her eyes pleaded with him for understanding. 'No. I don't blame you. Not at all. I'm just trying to tell you how I felt. As I look back on it, I can't blame you at all. It was my fault. I was always a push-over for you—a doormat. I can't blame you for walking all over me! But there were good times, Tim. I remember them well. Although—I could never go back to what we were. Never!'

CHAPTER SIX

TIM GOT UP from the table and walked over to the door, thumping one hard fist into the other open palm. 'And so that's why you hate me?' he asked.

She stood up and stretched both hands towards him, palms upward, in an appeal for understanding. 'No. I didn't hate you then, and I don't hate you now,' she said. She was trying to keep her voice firm, but failed badly. 'I don't really blame you for any of this, Tim. It was as much my fault as it was yours. Maybe more my fault. Please try to understand me.'

'I don't understand, Teresa, but I'll give it up for now. Perhaps just being here together we'll find—listen!'

'Listen to what? I don't hear anything.'

'That's what I mean. The wind has dropped. It's quiet.'

'Do you suppose that the storm is over?'

'I doubt it. I think the centre of it has just passed overhead. It might not last long. But there's a chance for us to get the generators going if we hurry. We need the power. I just can't sit here with all this going on and not have a single instrument activated to register anything. If you want to help, grab your outdoor gear!'

It took her fifteen minutes to locate all her cold-weather clothing and slip into it. When she came back out into the cold room he was at the roof hatch, struggling to push a massive roll of rope out into the snow. 'Bring that tool kit,' he called down to her. He stepped out of her view, and she followed him clumsily up the ladder, juggling the tool kit between both hands.

When she poked her head through the hatch she could see that the wind had dropped, but was still gusting, and the snow was falling almost straight down. The flakes were tiny, drifting slowly and whirling in circles when the gusts struck. She struggled out on to the roof of the cold chamber and closed the hatch behind her.

'For safety's sake we need to stretch a guide rope from here to the generator building,' he screamed in her ear. 'I have this end of the rope spliced on to the support beams of the trailer. Take this small piece of rope, tie it around your waist, and then tie the rest of the smaller rope in a loose circle around this big one. That keeps us both attached to the guide rope. Then, between us, we can carry the reel of rope, and start for the generator building. Got it?'

She shouted affirmation, but the wind whipped the words away. She fumbled at the knot, but found it impossible to tie with the heavy mittens on her hands. Before she could strip off the mittens his hands closed over hers, made the knot, and tested its strength by giving it a hard jerk. 'Okay?' he yelled. She nodded her head, and readjusted her face-mask.

There was a rudimentary set of snow-stairs from the roof of the trailer to the level of the island, but the new fall of snow had almost obliterated them. He gestured a 'follow me' signal with his right hand, then sat and slid down the incline to the base snow below. She duplicated the effort, but was unable to keep her feet in front, and suffered the ig-nominy of landing on her posterior. Tim helped her up and guided her hand to one side of the axle that ran through the centre of the reel.

The first few steps were easy. They were still in the shel-ter of the trailer, where the wind had little power, although the new loose snow had accumulated to knee depth. Far-ther out, where the wind had full control, the snow

amounted to almost nothing at all. He gestured in the
direction he wanted to go, where the roof of the generator
building could just barely be seen, and they started off,
playing out the rope as they went.

Each gust of wind struck her in the back of her knees with
the force of a sledgehammer. Twice she slipped and fell, but
scrambled back up again before he could help. Once a massive gust smashed her into his back, gluing her there like a
butterfly pinned to a display. He put an arm around her to
steady her, and then scanned the rapidly clouding area in
front of them.

'Over that way,' he yelled. 'I think I can see a corner of
the building!' He started to move again, and she struggled
to follow. Her face-mask slipped, almost blinding her. She
ploughed steadily forward, lifting each knee high in order
to swing her heavy boots clear of the snow. When she
bumped into him again he was laughing. 'We're here!' he
shouted at her. 'Get inside out of the wind!'

She dropped her share of the load and staggered towards
the door of the building, brushing snow out of her mask as
she did so. The latch on the door was a two-handed affair.
The door opened outwards, as most arctic doors do, so that
the winds help to seal the building shut, rather than blowing the doors open. Terry pulled with all her strength, but
the door did not move. She stamped out a better place to
stand, wrapped her hands around the latch, and tried again.
Nothing moved. Almost totally exhausted, she leaned
against the door and beat on it with her tiny fists. And then
he came.

'The guide rope is secure,' he yelled in her ear. 'Get
yourself untied—oh, never mind, I'll do it myself.' He
stripped off his gloves and wrestled with the knots that tied
her to the guide rope. The little safety line fell to the snow
as he braced his feet against the sides of the door and heaved
it open.

Terry stumbled towards the opening, and a hand in the middle of her back sent her sprawling inside, out of the wind. In a moment Tim joined her, and the door slammed heavily behind them, sped by another gust of wind.

He helped her up, brushed the outer fur layer of the hood of her parka, and laughed. 'My God, but you're beautiful,' he said.

'What are you—you must be mad,' she chuckled. 'You can't see anything of me but my eyes. Even my eyebrows are covered.'

'Oh, but I've had practice in Saudi Arabia,' he chortled. 'Once you learn to judge beauty from behind the veil, an arctic overcoat is child's play! Come on, take it off!' He swung a generous pat in the direction of her bottom, but managed to miss.

Terry pulled back her hood, slipped off her face-mask, and straggled off behind him. He was already at the generators, four of them, identical, set in a square. Somewhere he had found a large flashlight, and was using it to light his way around the machinery. His check-up required only minutes.

'The damn change-over switch is frozen,' he announced. They could talk normally now. The walls of the building cut down some of the noise of the wind. 'How about that for a triumph of engineering?'

'I haven't got the faintest idea what you're talking about,' she returned.

'We've got four generators,' he explained. 'Each one is supposed to run for eight hours, then switch another one on. The change-over switch up there on the wall is what does it all. It's got water on it, and froze in position.'

'Can you fix it?'

'Maybe. Can you see that blowtorch anywhere around?'

'I don't know, dear. I wouldn't know a blowtorch if it ran over and bit me. Does it bite?' No, it doesn't bite, you idiot, she told herself. Your mouth has come unhinged. Calling him 'dear'—you fool woman! But evidently he hadn't noticed.

'I've got it,' he muttered. He pumped on the pressure handle of the torch, cracked open the valve until something hissed, then lit a match and held it in front of the torch. A stream of fire flashed two feet in front of them. Terry screamed at the unexpected, then hurriedly apologised.

'Hey, don't apologise,' he grinned. 'I don't know another woman in the world who would have put up with what you've had to these last forty-eight hours. You do well!'

She turned her back so that he could not see the smile that spread across her face. Her first accolade! To be stored and treasured for ever and ever. And he almost sounds as if he likes me, she whispered to herself.

'See that big red switch marked *LOAD*,' he called to her. 'Pull it down. I'm going to see if I can unfreeze the change-over gear without burning the building down.'

'It would be a help,' she laughed. 'I'm just getting accustomed to the place. Is it possible?'

'To burn it down? You'd better believe it. It's highly probable. Fire is the biggest danger in the Arctic. Now, watch the master at work—I hope. We just give that thing a little touch of the fire, like so, and carefully let the heat spread, and then we reach up with one hand and—*voilà!* Damn it!'

'Did you hurt yourself?' she enquired.

'No. You're supposed to reach up and *"voilà"* with the gloved hand, not the bare one! But the switch is thrown, anyway.' He sucked at two of his fingers. 'And don't tell me about that being unsanitary, either!'

'I wasn't going to. I'm off duty now. And I don't give free or unsolicited advice. Can we start the generator now?'

'If I can figure out which one is—ah, this is the baby. Now, if the batteries are still charged, and the fuel line hasn't frozen, we'll—' He pushed the starter button on Generator

Number Three. The big engine groaned, squealed, coughed, and caught!

They looked at each other in astonishment as the light in the building came on. The generator grumbled a couple of times, then settled into a smooth purr. 'You marvellous man!' she yelled, and threw herself at him. The impact knocked them both to the wooden floor of the building, where she collapsed in his arms, laughing and crying at the same time.

'Well,' he concluded, 'there's nothing wrong with that sort of reception! Is that all?'

'No,' she laughed at him. 'I'm so relieved. I think I'll start a church when we get out of here. To worship Electricity! I'm so—' She had managed to strip off both gloves now, and she threw her arms around his neck, running her fingers through the soft silk of his hair, and then pulled his head down until his lips met hers. There was an instant spark! The mood of gaiety vanished, to be replaced by a driving urge to get closer to him, to squeeze herself into a bundle of emotions and offer it all to him. His arms came around her, strong, comforting, protective, and the tears rolled away. They were locked together for minutes, then she pulled away to find air to breathe.

'Oh my God, Teresa,' he groaned. 'Oh my God!'

She moved uneasily away from him, aware that she had uncorked the volcano, and afraid of when and how it might erupt. 'Hadn't we better get back?' she half whispered. He shook his head as if it were enveloped in cobwebs.

'Back. Yes,' he said. His voice was ragged with emotion. 'We'd better. Push that LOAD switch back into the other position, will you.' She struggled to comply, while he snooped around the generator looking for trouble. 'It's holding the load,' he assured her. I wish I was, Terry silently prayed.

Tim came back, a relieved smile on his face. 'Buckle yourself up again,' he said. 'It ought to be easier going back. Just make sure you hold on to the guideline. Right?'

In the event, the trip back was not easy at all. The wind was rising again, and driven snow cut into her face through the interstices of her mask, and powdered into her hood and down her neck. It took her twice as long before she staggered into the shelter of the trailers. He boosted her up to the roof entrance, and they dropped inside, where she collapsed on the floor, sitting yoga-fashion with feet crossed under her, and her back against the wall. All the lights were on inside, and she could hear a wild clatter of instruments from the radio room.

'Damn!' he muttered as he struggled out of his gear. 'I forgot to shut them off. I'll have to recalibrate the whole trailer-load. You all right?'

The last question obviously was a throw-away. She started to tell him exactly how she was, but by the time she had constructed a sentence in her mind, he was gone.

She hardly knew whether to laugh or cry, whether to be angry, or relieved. But sitting on the floor debating the subject was certainly no solution, so she managed to get herself upright, took off her outer gear, and wandered back to the kitchen. The trailer was beginning to rock again to the beat of the wild song that the wind has playing. She braced one hip against the counter, and glared at the leg of lamb. The clock already marked 1700 hours, five o'clock in the afternoon. She shrugged her shoulders in disgust, then found a carving knife and sliced some tiny pieces off the top of the joint. The curry powder she had noticed earlier was still trying to hide behind the salt jar. She rescued it, and started to work. By the time Tim had finished his calibrations and joined her, the dinner was sizzling hot, in more ways than one, and welcome.

He sighed and patted his stomach when he had finished. 'You didn't cook like that before?' he queried. 'I have a strange nostalgic memory of meals like that!'

'Not from me,' she laughed, as she got up to clear the table. 'Maybe from my mother. You remember?'

'Fine woman, Teresa. I knew you'd be like her when you grew up. That's why I married you!'

'Is that so?' she said, trying to sound nonchalant. 'I often wondered why. To tell the truth, I thought that it was—well, I must get these dishes clean. And I have to heat a pan of water tonight. I need a good wash.' A gust of wind stronger than usual slammed into the trailer, rocking the floor under their feet, and interrupting the conversation. He broke out his pipe and searched his pockets for tobacco.

'I'll see if I can contact anyone on the radio,' he told her. 'You go ahead. Take your time.'

She hummed a tune as she waited for the pan of water to bubble. If it were not for the insane rocking of the trailer I would be perfectly happy, she told herself. Or if it had been warmer in the generator building. If only I could turn back the clock and live all those bitter-sweet months again. If only! She reached for the pan as the water came to the boil, and managed to burn her fingers. She used a few select words that nurses sometimes overhear in the course of their duty, wrapped a towel around the handle of the pan, and wobbled her way over into the bath facility. She poured the water into the small steel washbowl, then walked back to be sure that the outer trailer door was closed. There was no hook or latch to fasten. The floor continued to rock under her feet.

She found two large towels in one of the drawers under the bunk-beds. She spread one on the floor, and draped the other over one of the exposed pipes. Hurriedly she stripped off her borrowed clothes and stood shivering in front of the bowl. The hot water was already cooling. She sponged herself off as best she could, making sure that both feet were carefully washed, and, more carefully, dried. In the back of her mind were the words from the Survival lecture, 'Your feet are your only mobility. Take care of them, and they'll take care of you.' The memory gave her a little giggle. It had all sounded so melodramatic in the classroom. But not here. Dear Lord, not here!

She struggled vainly to reach the itch in the middle of her back, but without success, no matter how she wiggled.

'Let me get that for you,' Tim said matter-of-factly from just behind her left shoulder. She gasped, snatched at her second towel, and tried madly to wind it around herself.

'What are—what do you think you're doing?' she shouted at him. 'Get out of here. Get out!'

'In just a minute,' he replied coolly. 'You know you can't reach there. You never could.' He took the wash cloth from her stiff hands. She grabbed at her towel, and held it up in front of her without even thinking that it was her back he was staring at. He dipped the cloth into the tepid water, added a little soap, and began a gentle massage of the dead-centre of her back. Every nerve end in her body seemed to have sprung to battle stations, and was flashing alarms to her brain. She was unable to still the trembling that seized upon her muscles. Gradually he increased the size of the circles, until he was sweeping in a wide gentle curve from her hips to her shoulders. She bit her lip, trying to suppress the wild driving emotions that his touch inspired.

He dropped the wet cloth, and tweaked the towel out of her hand. He moved closer as he dried her back, until she could feel the heat of him pressing against her. 'I want you, Teresa,' he said hoarsely, 'and you want me. Nothing has changed. Nothing!'

The words were like a splash of cold water, snatching her back from the brink. 'I don't want you or any man,' she snapped. 'Leave me alone!'

'You want me, Teresa,' he repeated. 'You want me!' His hands slipped around and over her shoulder blades and cupped her breasts. She gasped, and wrestled herself away from him. With fumbling fingers she weaved a sarong out of the bath towel, not daring to look at him.

'Years ago, maybe,' she muttered at him, 'but not now. Not any more. Leave me alone, Tim. If you touch me tonight it will be rape. Is that what you want it to be. Get out of my way. Leave me alone!'

His face flushed. She could feel his hand on her shoulder tremble. What am I doing, she yelled at herself. It's what I want. Why do I fight him! But she knew why. She had only to look at the fierce gleam in his eye, hear the wild hunting call in his voice. He was in the grip of passion, she was in the grip of love. If I give in to him now, she told herself, I'll be right back where I was six years ago. A doormat for him to trample on. A mindless slave to suit his passions, and then be put away in some cupboard until next time! She knew her pride could not stand such a blow, nor her intellect survive such a change. He was watching her, as if he could read her mind.

'I'm still your husband,' he reminded her bluntly.

'So you say,' she hurled at him. 'I've only your word for that. Your mother said differently. I believe differently. For six years I've done without you and your support. You and your so-called protection.'

'It doesn't alter the fact,' he said softly, dangerously. 'I want you. Now.'

'My God, are you mad? You think you're some imperial Caesar! You think that all you have to do is to snap your fingers and I'll fall down at your feet? Well, it won't happen.'

'It will happen,' he insisted. 'And you won't fight me. You'll enjoy it as much as I will. Don't fight me—it will only hurt you. I'm too strong for you.'

She slipped by him, but found herself trapped in the closed end of the trailer, beside her own bunk. She forced herself to breathe more slowly, to think more calmly. He was right—he was much stronger than she. Only logic would bring her out of this. Gradually she regained control over her emotions.

'So you want me,' she said coldly. 'What you mean is that you want a woman. Any woman. And I'm elected because I'm available! That's the way our life always was, wasn't it?'

'That's not true. Don't fight me, girl.'

'It *is* true. That's the only true thing about this whole situation. You want a woman. You're stronger than I am. And you think you have a piece of paper that gives you the right! Well, I can't fight you. You want me?' She dropped the towel to the floor and stood in front of him in all her cool naked beauty. His breath whistled as he inhaled quickly. She mustered a look of disdain as she moved over to her bed and stretched herself out flat on her back. 'You want me,' she repeated, 'then take me. But don't expect me to co-operate. It will be rape—and it will be the end of everything for us. You want me that way, Tim? Go ahead, force me!'

She closed her eyes and fixed a grim expression on her face. There was a moment of quiet, then she heard him come to the side of the bed.

'Look at me, Terry,' he commanded.

'No,' she moaned.

There was another moment of silence, and then she felt his fingers stroke her throat. The movement chilled her, sending her whole body into shivers of fear. It was not what she had expected. It wasn't rape he had in mind. He was going to do it now. A perfect place for it, cut off from the rest of the world, in the midst of one of the great arctic storms of the century. And who would miss one tiny woman in all the smashing triumph of *Götterdämmerung*!

'Don't be afraid,' he murmured. His hand disappeared from her throat, and she heard the rustle of clothing falling. The bed sagged near her hip, and she could feel the warmth of his skin pressing in on her. His hand appeared again, just below her knee, drawing tiny circles, and gradually moving upward along the inside of her thigh. Her nerves screamed for release, but she locked her lips and stiffened her body. That treacherous hand trailed lightly higher, across her abdomen, drawing circles on her tiny waist, and then marching inexorably up the curve of her breast until it touched gently on the bronze cone of her nipple and stopped there.

Terry fought back all the impulses to surrender, clenching her fists so that the pain from her own fingernails would provide a counterbalance. His hand continued, joined by the second, cupping both her breasts in tantalising strokes. Then the hands stopped. She felt the moist warmth of his breath against her tension-stretched skin, and was unable to restrain the jump that resulted when his lips closed on her breast, and his tongue teased its taut cap, driving her near to insanity! She had to do something. Do something! To lie still was to court simple surrender and disaster.

She opened her eyes and found his inches away. There was a satisfied smile on his face. She rearranged her jaw muscles to let a few words slide through her lips.

'Hurry up,' she told him coldly. 'I don't feel like waiting all night. Get it over with. You think of me as a whore, you might as well treat me like a whore.'

His hands snapped away from her as if they had been burned. The look of satisfaction turned to pure fury. 'Damn you,' he snarled. 'God damn you to hell!'

'He already has,' she answered bitterly, 'and I've been serving my sentence for years!'

He stumbled up from the bed and started to dress. 'This isn't over yet,' he swore. He snatched up his shoes without putting them on, and moved towards the door. 'It isn't over yet,' he promised.

'I know,' she said sadly. 'I'll be here. I'm not going anywhere.'

He slammed through the doorway, banging it closed behind him with enough strength almost to match the impact of the gusting winds outside. The noise broke her rigid control. She sat up in bed, and the tears ran like floodwaters down her pale cheeks, dripping off her chin on to her sore and distended breasts. What have I done, she asked herself. And dared not face the answer. He offered me all he had to give—all he had ever offered, and I refused him. It would have made me happy before, but now it's not enough. Although I have come to the end of the world, it is not—or is it, Teresa Alden? Feel the world rock and throb and pitch. There's a wild beast out there, raging to get at you both, raging to kill. And if this is the end of the world, would you have it end your way, or his?

Hurriedly she fought her way into the trousers and shirt she had claimed as her own. As she belted the pants about her she moved towards the door, looking for him. She found him sitting in the radio room, ears glued to the loudspeaker, where a lonely distant voice was giving a long-range weather forecast. He looked up as she came over to him. Even in that short space of time he had cooled down.

'What does he mean?' she asked hesitantly, waving towards the radio. 'I don't understand what he means.'

'What he means is that this storm is going to continue, and may get worse,' he said. 'The winds have long since passed gale force. The storm is almost motionless, stuck right over our heads.'

'But could—could anything happen? To us, I mean?'

'Lord, I don't know,' he said quietly. 'It's gone a long way beyond my experience. Something could happen. For the moment we're pretty safe. This island is four times bigger than any ocean liner, and as long as it's safe, we're safe. But you understand we have no control over what's going to happen. Look at all my instruments. All they can tell me is that we're in a lot of trouble. But they can't predict a thing about the future.'

He sighed and flipped the radio off. 'It isn't worth listening to any more,' he said. 'There's no help to be had until the storm ends.' He reached out a hand to steady himself against a particularly strong sway and jar of the trailer.

'You don't have to tell me the rest,' she told him. 'I can feel it. We're drifting free, aren't we? I can't believe that we could be sailing through solid ice. But we are, aren't we?'

'Yes, we are. The island is so big and so heavy that it's crushing its way through the ocean ice. But every inch we move, every chunk of ice we crunch under us, weakens the island itself. Well, it's no use worrying about it. There's nothing we can do about it.'

She slumped back against the lowest instrument shelf, folding her arms across her chest, and watching him as he fumbled with his pencil.

'Teresa,' he said. 'I'm sorry about all that stupidity in the trailer. You're right on all counts. I had meant it to be different. I needed you—very much. I had the mad hope that we could get together again, and solve all our problems. But I can see it won't happen. Okay, I give it up. It doesn't seem worthwhile to ask for forgiveness. But if ever you need me, for anything, you have only to call me. Understand?'

'I—I didn't mean everything I said,' Terry said softly. 'It wasn't all true. None of it. Your mother was right. You deserved more than me—more than you got. I'm as sorry as you are. My mother always told me that it was the woman's work to make a marriage go. And I failed you, not the other way around. Can we be—friends, Tim?'

'I don't think so, Terry. Not after what we've been to each other. Let's just get along here as best we can until the Air Rescue team shows up. And then we can go our separate ways. I don't—I won't bother you any more.'

She stood in front of him with head bowed, unable to muster the words to set them on the right course. He watched her for a moment, stretched out a single finger to touch the fringe of curls around her ear, then went back to his instruments. Infinitely weary, she dragged her feet slowly back to her bed, took off all her clothes, and slid under the

single sheet. The light glared in her eyes, but she paid it no
heed. The trailer was bucking and jumping now like a wild
thing. She closed her eyes.

'I need you,' he had said. Not 'I love you'—just 'I need
you.' And it was true. He had always needed her. She had
always needed him. And into the mutual need she had
woven the romantic fiction that he loved her. What a fool
you are, she lectured herself. Grow up for a change. If this
is all we have, share it. There will be a time for giving later,
after he has satisfied his need. And until then, there will
be—passion? Satisfaction?

And then the world of storms took over her mind. The
trailer bounced twice, sharply. The tortured metal groaned
under the pressure of the wind's contortions. She clutched
at the sides of the bed to hold herself in. The world seemed
to be filled with a high-pitched whistle, and with an
abruptness that terrified her, the lights went out again.

She lay frozen in her bunk, holding on for dear life. There
was a clatter at the door, and Tim came in carrying one of
the Coleman lanterns. The brilliant light comforted her. 'It's
only the generators again,' he said matter-of-factly. 'I guess
we might as well bed down for the night. I've shut everything else off. The plywood roof of the cold chamber is beginning to break loose. If it goes, the whole chamber will go,
and perhaps even one of the trailers. If that happens, we
can't afford the risk of fire from the heaters.'

'You've turned off the heat in this trailer, too?' she queried. 'We'll have no heat here either?'

'No. We daren't risk it,' he said quietly. 'It's only a precaution, not a real alarm. Only a precaution.'

'I—I see,' she stammered. The trailer jumped again,
throwing him against the wall. He regained his balance, and
hung the lantern on the hook beside her bed, where it
swayed back and forth in concert with the swaying of the
trailer. He withdrew beyond the circle of light and began to
undress. She could see him as a shadow, tall and brooding,

in the hissing light of the pressure lamp. He sat down on the edge of the opposite bed, and pulled back the covers. She mustered up her courage.

'No, Tim.' She had to shout to be heard above the crescendo of the wind. 'Over here. I think—this could be our last night. But even if it isn't, I want you by me.'

'Dear God, Terry, don't start that! You made your position clear earlier. And don't get carried away to doomsday in your calculations. I don't have any doubts about how you feel about me. And I'm not some damn plaster saint, to share your bed without laying a finger on you. You surely don't expect me to get into your bed and just go to sleep, do you?'

'I was wrong, Tim. Wrong about how I feel—about you, I mean. I don't want you to be a saint. I just want you. Please?'

He groaned and hesitated, then moved across the narrow aisle between them. She moved sideways in the narrow bed to offer him room. He slipped under the sheet with her, pressed against her total length by the confines of the bed. She cupped his face in her hands and gave him a gentle kiss, a kiss of memory and of promise. Slowly his hands coursed over her, drawing her closer, exciting her, mastering her. Until, unable to control his passions longer, he rolled on top of her.

He pushed himself up on his forearms and looked at her as she pantingly urged him on. 'Last chance, Terry,' he said hoarsely. 'Yes or no?'

'Yes, dear lord, yes,' she gasped, pressing upward against his aroused male strength. He lowered his weight on to her thighs and breasts—and there was a tremendous crackle of noise from outside, accompanied by a high-pitched shriek of metal in agony. Something smashed into their trailer, snapping them both off the bed and hurling them against the opposite wall. He cushioned her shock to his own damage. His back smashed into the wall and he went deadly quiet.

Terry could hear someone screaming. Her fists went up to her mouth, and she found the source of the noise.

Battered, frightened beyond reason, she managed to scramble to her knees. The trailer had not actually tipped over, but had been snapped as if it were the end of a whip, and was now vibrating back and forth, establishing a new equilibrium. She struggled to her feet. The floor trembled and grumbled, as if they were passing over some strange arctic life-form. And then there was another shock. Everything came to a stop, hurling Terry and all the loose contents of the trailer against the back wall. The floor lifted at an angle, and the loose equipment clattered down the new slope towards the door. The lantern made one last swing, bounced off the hook, and smashed itself into darkness. Neither of the passengers noticed.

CHAPTER SEVEN

SHE WOKE SLOWLY, in separate pieces. First a hazy mind, and then a command to each arm and leg, with a groaning response. Then she opened one eye, carefully. She was lying in her bunk, under a sheet and a pile of blankets. A Coleman lantern hissed on the table beside her bed, and a tiny light showed from the other end of the trailer through the window of the space heater. There was no noise, no movement, no rocking or swaying. She opened the other eye and the room came into focus. The trailer looked as if some giant hand had taken it, shaken it out, and left all its internal goods piled in the lower corner, next to the door, which opened slowly as she watched.

'Awake?' Tim called. He seemed to be climbing upward to where she lay.

'Alive?' she retorted.

'Very much so,' he assured her. 'It isn't as bad as it could be, by a whale of a lot.' She made a wry face at him. 'One of the trailers was tipped over and blown away. I can't see it at all. It's still snowing. After it stops we may be able to locate it. It's the one with Henry's body in it. I think he may be getting the Valkyrie funeral he deserves. Our space heater is working as well as ever. And you've got another crack on your head!'

'They say you can read your future by the bumps on your head,' she offered.

'Well, in that case you'll have a long adventurous life,' he chuckled.

'And you?' she asked anxiously. 'You hit that wall awfully hard. And I bounced off of you.'

'It knocked me out for a little while, but everything seems to be working. I think we'll both be a mass of bruises by tomorrow.'

'How is it outside?'

'Everything quiet. Still snowing, but coming down straight, in little clumps. Can't see the sun, but it's out there, just waiting for the last of these clouds to roll on. I have the feeling somebody's going to snap a switch pretty soon, and turn the world on for us!'

Turn the world on for us! Oh God! She sat up in the bed, drawing the sheets up to her neck to cover her nudity. He came over to the side of the bed and waited as she tried to overcome the knot in her stomach. 'Well?' he asked.

'I—last night,' she stammered, trying to hold back the tears that kept sliding down out of the corners of her eyes. 'I don't want you to think—I was—confused. I—'

'You don't have to explain it any further,' he said grimly. 'It's plain enough even for a dummy like me. Last night was all a terrible mistake, and nice girls don't do that sort of thing, and would I please forget the whole thing. Is that the story? How's your head?'

'I—yes. Please, Tim?' Her shadowed eyes, bigger than ever before in her tired, strained face, pleaded with him.

'You needn't ask, Teresa,' he said coolly. 'Feel like some breakfast?'

'I—I don't think I could make—'

'I'll be the cook. I think we've got enough propane for three or four more days. Would ham and powdered eggs do?'

'Ugh. Well, and coffee? Toast?'

'No toast. We're out of bread entirely, and I haven't had a chance to bake any.'

'You, Tim? You, baking bread. I don't believe it.'

'Yeah. Seems funny, huh? There've been changes since the old days. I told you that.'

'I know. I can see.' She tried hard to keep the wistful note out of her voice, but to no avail.

'You get dressed. I'll start the fixings. Better put on some heavy clothes. There are a few draughts here and there.' One of his fingers gently touched against her breast, tapped the nipple, then coursed upward to her chin. He tilted the chin up and kissed her briefly and gently, and then left.

It took her longer to dress than she had anticipated. Every muscle ached, and cramming herself into her thermals became a struggle. She compromised. Over the thermals she slipped on her Inuit trousers, and for her feet, only the inserts to her mucklucs. The braces, looping over her shoulders, outlined her full breasts more than she wanted. She loosened the straps, praying that the trousers would stay up, if only by God's will. There was a hairbrush in the bathroom compartment. She brushed hard, until the glossy black sheen of her curls sparkled. Then she made her way down the slope, and out into the cold room.

One entire wall of the room had disappeared, along with the trailer that once had projected through it. Tim had been busy. A heavy tarpaulin hung crudely over the opening, scaling out most of the wind, and some of the snow. She hugged herself to still the shivers, and turned back to the little kitchen. Tim came in behind her, carrying a package from the food storage trailer.

'Snow's almost stopped,' he told her as he dished up the breakfast. 'Scrambled eggs. The only honest thing you can do with powdered eggs. But the ham is real, and there's plenty of it. Our only real shortage is water.'

'I meant to ask you about that,' she said, scooping up a forkful of warm ham.

'Nothing to it, really,' he replied. 'We have a big barrel on the roof. We fill it up with snow, and turn on the heat, and get water. But a heck of a lot less water than there was snow. Be sparing, be sparing.'

'I will. But you'd better eat something quick. It ought to be time to call Thule on the radio.'

'Not a chance,' he mumbled, his mouth half-full of food. 'We don't have any working radios. Everything we have requires generator power. And that we ain't got.'

'And we—we just. We just sit here until somebody decides to come and find us. That's it, isn't it?'

'Yup. Shouldn't be long. Have some more ham.'

'Tim—I want to talk to you about last night.'

'You don't have to explain anything, Terry. You thought it was our last night on earth, and you're a sensitive soul and I understand. I won't try to take advantage of you.'

'It isn't that, Tim. I don't know if I can explain myself, or if I even understand myself. I have the feeling—the feeling that you and I are strangers, Tim. You're not the man I knew, and I'm not the woman you knew. I've said some terrible things to you. When I'm mad I'm a terrible bitch. I didn't—I don't mean anything of that—not anything I said.'

'Which one is the real Terry Alden? The one who pushed me out of her bed, or the one who pulled me in?'

'I—what I'm trying to say is that neither is the real me. Neither one. I don't intend to hop into your bed, but I don't intend to call you names, either. It's been a long time for us, and I have a lot of memories. But in spite of that, or perhaps because of that—I—I like you very much, Tim. That's all I know. Could we go back to square one, and just try to get to know each other all over again?'

'A cautious truce? My name is Tim Alden. I'd like to get to know you better. Would you like to go to bed with me?' He stuck out his hand and smiled.

'Not like that,' she laughed. 'No, I don't. I don't think I—now you're just getting me mixed up!' She put her right hand into his paw, and watched it disappear. If only it could be like this, she prayed. If only we could be light-hearted, and overlook the past.

'Don't get flustered,' he chided her. 'I know what you mean. You don't mind if I come to court you?'

She pulled back her hand and fumbled some more food into her mouth. 'No, I don't mind, Mr Alden. I think I might feel honoured.'

'In that case,' he laughed, 'flowers for *madame*.' He put a page from a magazine down beside her plate. It was a full-colour portrait of a bunch of roses.

'Oh—you—that's nice,' she stammered. She picked up the picture, caught it in the loose strands of her suspenders, and smiled back at him. 'I shall treasure your flowers next to my heart,' she promised. They both laughed, a satisfied companionable laugh that promised more—in the future.

'And now if you'll hurry,' he told her when the breakfast was over, 'I'll take you on a scenic stroll along the beautiful beaches of the Arctic Ocean.'

She dipped him a curtsey and ran for her outdoor gear. He was waiting for her in the cold room when she came back. 'We might as well take the short cut,' he told her, lifting the edge of the tarpaulin aside. She stepped out into the snow and stopped to wait for him. The precipitation had stopped, and a quiet surrounded them. High-level winds were still whipping clouds across the sky, but occasional patches of blue showed, and a glint of sunlight. At their lower level nothing seemed to stir, and there was enough light available to make the scene resemble a cloudy day in the mountains back home.

'Look at this.' He was dangling an unravelled segment of rope in front of her. She pulled down her face-mask and took a close look. 'It's the end of our guide rope to the generator building. I suspect the worst, Mrs Holmes.'

'Sherlock, are you trying to frighten me?'

'Not me, lady. Stick with me—close—and we'll go and have a good look. Step where I step.' He was carrying a long thin pole in his hand, and was using it to feel out the surface in front of them before they stepped. Gradually they inched their way in the direction of the generators. He walked in front, she directly behind, trying to put her feet into the prints he was making. When he stopped she had her head down, and ran into his back.

'What's the matter? Is the power house wrecked?' she shouted.

'No.' He stepped aside so that she could see. Instead of the building she had expected to see, they had come to the edge of the island. Straight down, a matter of forty or fifty feet, she could see the dark grey of the newly formed sea ice. 'We haven't lost the power building,' he commented, 'we seem to have lost the island. I was afraid of that. We'd better make a complete tour, and see how much island we have left.'

'You mean the island is breaking up?'

'Has broken,' he laughed. 'Don't worry about it. It's already over, and we're still alive. All it means now is that we have a much smaller estate.'

'And it's tilted, isn't it.'

'Yes. I guess that wherever we are, our part of the island has run up on something—a rock, a ledge, or even a shoreline. Come on, my dear, this beach is not too hospitable. Did you bring your bikini?'

'I—are you trying to cheer me up, Tim?'

'Who me?' He pulled her to a stop and drew her closer. 'One thing I've learned about you is that you don't give up easily, you don't scare easily, and don't need cheering up. Do you?'

'Thank you,' she said softly. 'Yes, I do.'

It took them a long foot-slogging hour to tramp the perimeter of their new domain. They ended up where they had started, next to the trailers. The sun had broken through the clouds, sending rainbow sparkles through the shattered ice crystals underfoot. He helped her in through the tarpaulin, stopping outside only long enough to look up at the sky.

They both stripped off their outer clothes, then made for the kitchen. Terry prepared two mugs of instant coffee, watching Tim as he studied the top of the table, tapping his forefinger on the cigarette-scarred surface. She sat down opposite him, coddling her mug between her hands.

'Bad?' she suggested.

'Not too bad, but bad,' he agreed. 'The good part is that we're aground on something. Our last fixed reading was just opposite the mouth of Robeson Channel, so I have to assume that we're close to the tip of Greenland. That's the good part. On the other hand, we've lost all the runway, all the lights, and all the beacons. There's no way a plane could land here to pick us up, and we're too far from Thule for a helicopter rescue. That's the bad part. And then there's the third piece to the puzzle. I don't know how far away the rest of the island is. If it's in one piece, they could land on it, and we could trek over to them. How's that?'

'Are you sure that the ocean ice will freeze again, strong enough to hold our weight?'

'Of course. It's four below zero out here. It's freezing already. Give it another six or eight hours and it would hold an elephant, never mind a little girl like you.'

'And then we'll just promenade over there. Should I pack my bags, do you suppose, or is this just a day trip?'

'That's my gal,' he chuckled. 'Now, there's a sled in the generator—oh hell, that's gone. Well, there are a couple of A-frame packs in here somewhere. Just in case, we'll get the packs ready, sort out what food we want to carry, hunt out the best maps of the area—and be prepared. You look for the A-frames. I'll sort out the stuff we'll need to carry.'

They both worked at the sorting—discarding, repacking—until two-thirty in the afternoon, and then they heard the noise. He stopped her babbling by covering her mouth with his hand. 'Aeroplane!' he said. 'Where the devil is that flare-gun. It was right here a minute ago. Where did you put it?'

'Right on that chair. Right where you left it,' she said innocently. He glared at her, then smiled, grabbed the gun, and ran for the outside. She followed, taking time to snatch her parka off the hook, and bringing his, too. The sky was completely clear now, and the sun was shining just above the horizon to their south. He slapped a cartridge into the gun, pointed it upward and to the north, and pulled the trigger. The flare dragged its trail of fire in a steep arc, and then burst open into a bright red ball of fire. He had already crammed a second cartridge in the gun by that time, and a third shot followed.

They could see the aircraft, a tiny speck winging above at fifteen thousand feet in a search pattern. It changed from a dot to a silhouette as it turned back towards the flares, and then began to lose altitude rapidly. When he fired the fourth flare the aircraft went into a steep dive. In minutes it screamed over their heads at a hundred feet, climbed sharply, and began to circle them.

'What's he doing?' she asked anxiously. 'Why doesn't he go and report? What's he doing?'

'Don't lose your cool,' he assured her. 'That's just what he's doing. Haven't you ever heard of radio? Just hold tight until he gets his instructions.'

'Well, put your parka on before you get frost-bitten,' she nagged. 'You'd think you would know better than to rush out here without your coat!'

'Yes, mother,' he teased, slipping his arm into the heavy coat. They traced the circles of the aeroplane with anxious eyes, stamping out a circle in the snow beneath their feet as they tried to keep the circulation going. Evidently the pilot quickly received his instructions. The plane turned in a lazy bank, its flaps extended, and it began a slow dive towards them. They could see the rear clam-shell door open, and the wheels came down.

'He can't land here,' she shouted in alarm. 'Do something, Tim. Tell him!'

'With what, smoke signals? He's not trying to land. He's trying to slow down, so he's putting out all the wind resistance he can find. I think they're—yes, they dropped something. Two somethings. Come on, Terry, run! You follow the one with the yellow parachute, and I'll chase the other. Don't let it blow off the island!'

Tim gave her a shove in the right direction, and they both took off at full speed. The little yellow parachute was close to her, settling gently, but still moving slowly towards the cliff that was the end of their island. It swept over her head just out of reach. She gathered all her leg muscles and jumped. Her hand barely managed to snatch at a trailing rope, and the parachute began to pull her along with it. She dug in her heels, wrapping both arms around the box to which the rope was attached. The parachute seemed to struggle against her weight, then gave up and collapsed on to the ice. She sat down suddenly, clutching at the box as if it were the Queen's jewels. A box! She wiped the wind-tears from her eyes, then put her mind back in gear and began to figure a way to get the box opened. It proved to be simple. The cardboard sections of the cover were only interleaved each with the other. Inside, packed in the centre of a bed of plastic cones, was a small hand radio. Attached to it was a paper with the number '4' crayoned on both sides.

She pulled the radio out of the box, and ducked as the airplane zoomed low over her head again. What next? She made a frantic search around her. Tim was still chasing down his parachute at the far end of the island. She held the radio up in front of her. It had three switches and a dial, but none of them meant anything to her. She had seen one on a desk during her basic training cycle. Seen it, and listened as the instructor talked, but had not been allowed to touch it.

And then she was rescued by memory. Her youngest brother, playing at 'Spaceman', with a little toy CB radio in his hand. You pull out the antennas, then hold the radio up to your ear—or mouth—and push the switch. She did, watching warily as the long metal antenna swayed above her head. She pushed the switch again. Nothing happened.

Wearily she lowered the radio and looked it over. Two tears fell on to the radio and splashed across a little knob. She wiped them off with her glove. Under the knob a red sign said 'Off-On'. It was off. She remedied that. The radio hummed for a moment, and crackled at her. She put it back to her mouth again, her thumb on the switch. She pushed, and the noise disappeared.

'Hello—' she said hesitantly. 'Hello—aeroplane?' There was no response, no noise. She shook the set and repeated. 'Hello aeroplane! Damn. I can't make this thing go!' She took her thumb off the switch and the noise returned. A voice crackled suddenly at her, a laughing male voice.

'Hello, Ice Lady. This is the aeroplane! You're doing fine. Just remember that you have to take your finger off the switch before I can talk back to you. Who is this?'

'This is me—I mean—I—me!'

'Well, since we've only got one lost girl, is this Lieutenant Alden?'

'Of course it is,' she replied indignantly. 'Who did you expect? Are you going to rescue us now?'

'Pretty soon, Ice Lady, pretty soon. Now, what's your condition?'

'I—we—we're all fine, except that Mr Merryweather is dead and Major Gorton is dead and we've lost the bodies, but Tim and I are all right, and—'

A heavy hand reached over her shoulder and gently disengaged her hand from the transmitter. With one hand Tim raised the transmitter to his mouth. With the other he pulled her up out of the snow and held her close to him.

'Air Force Rescue,' he said, 'this is NASA 82. We have two survivors, in good health. We have food for approximately five days, and no urgent, repeat, no urgent problems. The major part of the island broke off from us during the night. I do not, repeat, do not know its location. All instruments, beacons and power are out of service. Over.'

The return voice had lost its chaffing tone, and adopted a formal code. 'Damn all men,' she told herself in an undertone. 'Making fun of me. Just because I can't operate his darn radio. I hope I get him in hospital, the wise guy!' She had missed the complete transmission.

'Air Rescue, understand,' Tim was saying. 'Establish beacon and be prepared for further instruction at 2200 hours. Wilco. Out.' He pushed the antenna down into the radio case, turned the set off, and shoved it into the pocket of his coat. 'Come on, Terry. Let's get the beacon out and on the air.'

He started to walk away, but she was standing still, watching the aircraft dwindle. 'Oh! They're going away. They're leaving us. Tim! Do something!' she wailed.

'I am doing something,' he laughed. 'Come on now, Terry. You've done fine so far—better than any other woman I know of.'

'Better than any woman!' she scoffed at him. 'You are a chauvinist, Tim, and—' But she lost the rest of the words to the wind as he grabbed her hand and towed her after him towards the second parachute. Together they unpacked the slightly larger box, and pulled out a sealed steel container. A sharp spike protruded from its bottom.

'It's a Mark 7 beacon,' he explained as he hauled it out of the box. He looked around for a clear piece of ice, and rammed the spike into it.

'Oh really,' she said under her breath. 'Everybody knows that. What in the world is a Mark 7 beacon?' He looked up from where he was examining switches on the machine's side, and wiggled a finger at her.

'Among other things, Mrs Alden, I have remarkably good hearing!'

'For a man your age,' she said automatically, repeating a favourite joke of her grandfather's which they both had shared. 'So what is it going to do. Sing a song? Dance? Dispense soft drinks?'

He stood up, brushing the snow from his gloves. 'Is there such a thing as a female chauvinist?' he asked. He grabbed her arm and pushed her towards the trailer. 'What Mark 7 is going to do for us it to broadcast our location. First it's going to tell the satellite. And then the satellite is going to mark our position, so that the aeroplane, if it ever comes back, will be able to find us!'

'I'm sorry, Tim,' she apologised. 'It's just that sometimes I get overwhelmed by everything technological around here. *If* they come back? You think they might not come back?'

'Oh, somebody will come back. But that was a C-130. It's a pretty expensive bird to use just to find two people.'

'Thank God for that,' she sighed as they struggled past the tarpaulin and into the relative warmth of the trailer. Their feet took them automatically to the kitchen, and she automatically produced two more cups of coffee.

'You must think me a terrible dunce,' she mused, as she sat across the table from him.

'No such thing,' he chuckled. 'You've done fine. I can't think of anyone I would rather be stranded on an ice island with. That's not very good English. You make fine coffee, lady.'

'Even if it's instant?'

'Even if it's instant.' He propped up his chin with both hands and stared at her. 'You've got a lot going for you. Nice looks, beautiful cook, charming companion, good steady head. How come somebody like you isn't married already?'

She could feel the atmosphere suddenly change. The lightness, the humour were gone, replaced by a heavy silence. He was asking her something with more than just words, and she knew it. She ruffled a hand through her curls, trying to find the right words, trying to restore the light mood.

'I did get married once,' she almost whispered. 'I married Sir Galahad. And then I was kidnapped by the Wicked Witch of the West and penned up in a tower until I could get my head changed.'

'And Galahad hasn't found you yet?'

'Not yet.' She gulped at her coffee and scalded her throat. Silence hung over them, brooding, all-enveloping. He broke it with a new subject, for which she sighed gratefully.

'Why don't you tell me how you came to be a nurse?'

'Oh, well—there isn't much to tell,' she responded, more than pleased to get his mind off the original subject.

'So tell me, anyway.'

'I—well, I was in the hospital. As a patient. I told you about that.'

'With your hand?'

'No. Later. I was in the hospital, and I met Dr Weeks. You remember him. He was the school doctor for the football team, and the like. Orthopaedics. Well anyway, he remembered me. He came to see me several times, and we talked about medicine. And then after—and then when I got out of the hospital, he got a waiver for me. For my hand, you know.'

'No, I don't know. I know as much about nursing as you know about Mark 7 beacons.'

'Well, nurses have to have two hands—and my left hand was still—was still not working right. So he got me a waiver, and I was accepted at Massachusetts General for the two-year programme. It was terribly hard. You know I never was a scholar, but I knew I had to make it. The worst part of it was the expense. Papa's boat was making good catches, but the price of fish at the auctions was dropping lower and lower. And then, because I needed the money, he and the boys made that extra trip, and then—I told you about that.'

'He was a good man, Teresa. I respected him very much.'

She fumbled with a handkerchief, twisting it into unrecognisable shapes between her fingers. 'Yes,' she responded. 'Isn't that funny? That's just what he said about you.'

There was a reflective silence. 'And then?' he prodded.

'Well, the insurance took care of Mama. We never did find Papa and boys. And I got a loan from the bank, and a loan from the Luzo-American Society, and a gift from our Parish. And I had a job at McDonald's during the holidays. And—well, I graduated. Not at the top of the class.'

'And that's all there was to it?'

'Oh lord, no. A week after graduation I had to sit for the examinations for the State Board of Nursing. And with a lot of luck, I passed. And they gave me my licence. And that's how I became a Registered Nurse! I was so proud, Tim. It was the first thing I'd ever done by myself for myself. And I didn't have anyone to tell about it. Does that sound complicated?'

'No, that's pretty easy to understand. You worked hard, and did it all yourself. And at the end you had this lifetime licence to practise nursing. Grand!'

She looked at him suspiciously. 'You're not—making fun of me, Tim?'

'No, not at all,' he returned. 'I'm truly proud of you. I wish I could have been there.'

'You almost were,' she giggled, and then stifled it.

'And just what does that mean?'

'I—nothing. It means nothing.'

'Come on. Explain.'

She stared at the table, unwilling to meet his eyes. He prodded again.

'All right,' she muttered. 'When I got back to my room that night your detective had been there. I got out early the next morning. Just as my cab was driving away, yours came up behind us, and stopped. You almost made it.' Her voice dropped to a whisper. She shrank back in her chair.

He sat in silence for a while, staring into the bottom of his coffee cup. He's picked up something, she thought to herself. What did I say wrong? He's too sharp. I daren't try to outsmart him!

'So what happened after you got your licence?' he resumed.

'Nothing much,' she said. 'I went to Chicago. They accepted my Massachusetts licence. I worked the night shift, and went to the University in the daytime. And then—I—I decided to go to Denver, and I did the same there. And I got my Bachelor's degree at the University of Colorado. You never thought I would get a college degree, did you?'

'No, I never did,' he laughed. 'So you got your degree. What does that entitle you to do?'

'You mustn't be so haughty,' she chided him. 'I am a Bachelor of Science in Nursing. I am entitled to do nursing, to teach nursing, and to quote Shakespeare during any operation over one hour long!'

'You must quote me some, one day. Now tell me, what were you in the hospital for for the *second* time?'

'I need another cup of coffee. Would you like one?' She jumped from her chair and turned on the gas under a pan of water. 'Do you want one?' she repeated over her shoulder. He growled at her. So she made two cups, and brought them back to the table very, very slowly, hoping that the subject would have changed by the time she got there. It had.

'This Society that gave you the money,' Tim began.

'The Luzo-American Society. It was a loan. I'm paying it back by deductions from my salary. That's one of the reasons I volunteered for Thule. There's no place to spend any money up here, and I ought to be able to save a bundle.'

'I wish you had come to me for the money. I've got plenty. Mother left everything to me.'

'That's nice for you. You know I couldn't come to you.'

'I don't know anything yet. Really. Did you ever think of it?'

'Coming back, you mean?'

'Yes. Did you ever think of coming back to me?'

'I—yes. Yes, I thought about it a lot. In fact, when they sent me to San Antonio for training, I detoured by Houston. I don't know what I was thinking of. I went to—to the house, and I rang the doorbell, and a little girl answered. She said she'd never heard of the Alden family! I didn't stay—in Houston, I mean—I drove all night, and checked in at Lackland Field the next morning. And you?'

'Me? I stayed in Houston for a year after you left, then transferred to the Cape. I sold the house. I swore I'd never live there again. And then there were the moon shots, and the shuttle programme, and I've managed to get my Doctorate, along with a title as Project Research Officer. And here I am.'

'No. My mother kept hounding me to do it. She had a girl lined up for me, but I couldn't see that.'

'Why not?'

'Well, when you've had the best, you don't want seconds, Teresa.'

'Oh, what a lovely thing to say. Thank you, Tim.'

'And you? You thought you were divorced. I suppose you've got someone special lined up. Or half a dozen?'

'No. Not a one, Tim. It never crossed my mind. I treasured—' She stopped up her mouth before the rest of the words came out. I treasured your ring and your love, she had been about to say. But she held it back. She had talked too much already. All the chaff was out of the way. There was only one more subject they could possibly talk about, and if she brought that up, it could be the death of her. The thought sent shivers down her spine, and he noticed.

He stood up, touched a tender finger to her curls, and made for the door. 'I want to check the instruments. To see if there's anything we can salvage. Maybe we could take a few of the reports and films with us when they evacuate. What do you plan to do?'

'I—I guess I'll clean up the kitchen and take a nap. Or something. My head still aches a little. Do we have something unfrozen for dinner tonight?'

'Always the housewife!' Tim smiled. 'Don't worry about that. I'll take care of the supper. And get a good rest. They'll be looking for us with the radio at 2200 hours, and it might be our marching orders.'

'How much is that in American money?'

'2200? That's ten o'clock, ninny.'

She watched him walk out, then turned to the dishes. A few swipes completed the task. But why bother, she asked herself. You are going to walk away from all this—abandon it all to the Arctic ocean. And her mother's voice pounded in her ear. 'Never leave a dirty house,' the voice echoed. She laughed as she climbed the incline to her bed.

The Coleman lantern needed pumping. She gave it a few strokes, then lay back on the pillow and rested her eyes. Now he knows everything. Almost everything. Was it possible that his mother had lied about it all? If so—if he didn't know—what would happen if she told him the one thing he did not know? He had a quick, terrible temper. The chances were that even if he had not planned it before, he would do it the moment he heard. Guard your tongue, she told herself. Don't ever tell him. Give him up. Don't tell him.

Slowly the active thoughts faded away, dropping her deep into a restless grey world, where fears wore masks, and death was only make-believe. Deep in sleep, released from all conscious control, she tossed and mumbled and whimpered. When he came in she was rolling from side to side on the bunk. 'Call Joshua,' she was mumbling. 'Bring me Joshua!' And the pain in her voice, the longing, the loving, reached up like a fist and slapped him hard across his face.

CHAPTER EIGHT

IT WAS ALL THE EXERTION in the crisp cold air that had done it. She slept through dinner, and through the night, missing the second radio contact, as well as the fine stir-fried steak which Tim had prepared and set aside. When he woke her up at nine o'clock in the morning she felt refreshed for the first time since she had come to Greenland.

'Have I missed everything?' she asked. 'I didn't mean to leave all the work to you!'

'You haven't,' he returned cheerfully, 'but it's such a beautiful clear day outside, and I didn't want you to miss the sun. Besides, the equipment flight will be overhead within the hour, and we've a lot of work before us. Hurry up!' He slapped at her bottom, only partially concealed among the tousled blankets, and went back to the kitchen. She joined him quickly, wearing another pair of borrowed men's trousers, and a tentlike flannel shirt.

'I swear, Teresa, you'd grace a circus tent if you were wearing it,' he announced. He had prepared more of the powdered eggs, and four slices of bacon.

'It feels like a circus tent,' she said mournfully. 'Sometimes a girl wants to look beautiful for breakfast.'

'Oh? Well, you've made it. Eat up. This is the last of he bacon.'

'Hadn't we better save it then. For—for whatever?'

'Nope. We've got our walking papers. What we can't eat we leave behind.'

'You mean—you're just trying to scare me, aren't you?' Her frightened voice begged a negative.

'Not like that,' he assured her as he munched a bacon strip. 'I made radio contact with Air Rescue last night, and again this morning at six. Want to hear about it?'

'Not if it's bad news. I don't want to hear—well, yes I do.'

'Attagirl. So—there's a small problem at Thule. The only thing that can come for us and sit down around here is a helicopter. They've got one on line, and one coming up from Sonderström. The trouble is that the biggest of them has a fully-loaded range of only five hundred miles. We're just over five hundred and seventy miles away from them. So here's the scheme. They will use the two helicopters to establish a fuel dump at Cape Agazziz—that's just about halfway between us. They'll have to make several trips from Thule before Cape Agazziz is ready. Then they'll strip down one of the choppers, load it with maximum fuel, and come and get us. How's that!'

'Why that's grand, Tim. We go in comfort all the way! Oh, I like that. I'm lucky to be stranded with such an important person. If it were only me, I imagine I'd have to wait until the Inuit could come for me in a *kayak*.'

'In an *umiak*,' he corrected her. 'A *kayak* is strictly a one-man hunting boat. The *umiak* is that open boat you saw at Etah. It can carry twenty or thirty. And the women do the paddling.'

'Oh, you'd like that, wouldn't you,' she laughed. He didn't respond. 'What is it? There's something else, isn't there. Tell me. I'm more scared of not knowing, than—please?'

'On the line all the way, aren't you!' He laughed this time, and there seemed to be a gleam of tenderness in his deep-set eyes. 'Well, here it is. That little expedition I sketched will probably take from two to three weeks to be complete. So that means you and I have to take a little walk to a more convenient bus stop.'

'A little walk? In the middle of the ocean? They're mad! Are we supposed to paddle our island somewhere?'

'Hold on, Tiger. The satellite has taken four separate fixes on our present position. We're now aground fourteen miles from Foot Peninsula on Nyboesland, at the very top of Greenland. The ocean between us and the land is solidly frozen. The plane has made infra-red picture runs all the way. We can't stay here. The brains back there tell me that our little island is tilted, and has two major cracks down the middle of it. It'll be fine for a time, but any repetition of that storm, and this thing is liable to crumble.'

'And so we just get off and walk over to the subway station on—Nyboesland?'

'Well, so to speak, that's just what we do. At the tip of the peninsula is an old weather station which was closed down a year ago. It was left as an emergency base. It has two houses, and ample coal supply, water, and enough rations for two years. All we have to do is walk over there. We don't even have to turn on the steam or start the boiler. Somebody else is being dropped in there today by parachute, to do the housekeeping.'

'That's silly. Then there'll be three of us to rescue!'

'Not as silly as you think. One of the most important things he's going to do is to turn on the lights on top of the radio tower. The biggest problem about our taking this walk is getting ourselves lost. Once we get down on the sea ice it's going to be difficult to see anything. But if we can see the lights, we'll be okay. If not—we could wander around for days, and lady, it's cold outside!'

'And—you're sure that we can just climb down and stroll over there. The ice will all be frozen?'

'If it isn't the joke will be on us, won't it!'

'I—I—yes, it will be—funny, won't it. Was that what you were afraid to tell me?'

'Yes. I still am not accustomed to the fact that you're not a rabbit any more, Teresa. If the ice holds, and it ought to at this time of year, we'll just take a long slow walk, and be there in—ah—two days, perhaps.'

'That long? Only fourteen miles?'

'Yes. The ice will not be all that smooth. It isn't a skating rink out there. We'll find a good many flat areas. And we'll also find a lot of pressure ridges, a lot of mini-bergs to detour around, and perhaps a lot of snowdrifts in some areas. But we'll have plenty of light. This is the twenty-sixth of April. The sun will be above the horizon twenty-four hours a day from now on. Not overhead, you understand. It will be low on the horizon, circling around us. And when it's to our south it might drop behind mountains, low clouds, that sort of thing. Don't worry about it.'

'I'm not worried, Tim. I know you will get me there—if you want to.'

'That's a curious way of putting it.'

'I—I don't mean anything by it. I'll follow you anywhere you lead.'

'Just outside will do for now. Get your outdoor gear. The plane is going to drop us some equipment for the trip, right after they parachute the man into Nyboesland.'

They both scrambled into their parkas and went out into the sunshine. The brightness of it, after the gloom of windowless trailers, caught Terry by surprise. 'Here, try these.' He handed her a pair of dark snow-glasses. 'Going snow-blind is not fun,' he said.

And at just that moment the aircraft announced itself, coming in barely fifty feet above the level of their island, with its rear doors already open. As it passed the leading edge of the island a parachute deployed behind it, pulling a load of material out of the back of the aircraft. The parachute's only duty was the pulling. The pallet fell free and landed with a thump, skidding across the ice with the still-inflated parachute acting as a brake. Terry started out for the package, only to have Tim hold her back. 'They'll make one more pass,' he told her. 'Keep out of the way. No telling where anything will land after the drogue chute pulls it out of the plane.'

The aircraft came around again, this time even lower than before, and a second parachute pulled a package out of the plane and thumped it down on the ice. Tim handed her the small radio. 'Tell them we've got it all,' he said as he moved off towards the newly-landed material.

With less than her usual assurance Terry pulled out the antenna, turned on the switch, and stood shivering as her mind went blank. She knew there was a procedure to follow, but for the life of her she could not remember. She pushed the switch in, cutting out the noise, and said hesitantly, 'Hello, aeroplane. Hello, aeroplane?' and released the switch.

'Hello, Ice Lady,' the voice came back to her. 'This is the Postman. Is the delivery complete?'

'Yes. Yes.' She had regained her confidence. 'Is there any postage due?'

'I don't think so, Ice Lady. Charlie has reached the Weather Station. He reports by radio that the lights will be on in four hours, repeat, four hours. Do you plan to make your stroll today?'

'Can you—that's silly. I was going to say please hold the phone. I have to ask—I have to ask my husband.'

'Oh my, Ice Lady, you've just ruined breakfast for five people up here. We didn't even know you were married!'

She ran to Tim, busy unpacking one of the pallets. 'They want to know if we are going to start walking today,' she panted. He smiled at her and took the radio.

'Air Rescue, this is NASA 82,' he said. 'We expect to re-pack and climb down to ocean level today, if weather reports confirm good weather. We will move out for a few miles tonight, and begin the second part of the walk early tomorrow. Do you confirm weather?'

'Weather confirms, three days clear and cold, followed by snow on day four. Large cyclonic disturbances after that date. Thule recommends earliest movement, with all speed. Over.'

'Air Rescue, Roger. Wilco.'

He telescoped the antenna and put the set in the pocket of his parka. The aeroplane, whose voice had been at Terry's ear only a moment ago, had already become a tiny speck. She shook her head sadly, and waved to it anyway.

Working together they were able to unstrap the loads from the pallets without trouble. 'This thing is a sled,' he told her. 'Made of light-weight aluminum, with stainless steel runners. Looks okay. Weighs about twenty pounds, empty.'

'But the dogs to pull it are conspicuously absent,' she mourned.

'Whoof!' he returned. 'You and me, baby. Of course if we were real Inuit I would ride on the sled and my woman would pull!'

'That'll be the day!' Terry said disgustedly. They went over to the other pallet, jibing at each other.

'Food,' Tim pointed out. 'Water. Sleeping bag, and furs, arctic tent. Rifle.'

'Rifle? What do we need a rifle for?'

'Well, it's getting close on spring. We may not be the only beasties wandering around on the ice. Nice old gun. A modified Springfield 30-06. It'll stop one if we meet one.' He flicked the bolt of the rifle back and forth, testing it.

'Well? Drop the other shoe,' she demanded indignantly. 'It'll stop what one if we meet one?'

'Polar bear,' he returned. 'A couple of them were observed by the aeroplane early this morning. And rope, lots of rope!'

She was still shaking her head as he directed the packing of the sled. It was noon before they were finished, and everything lashed down tightly. They went back into the trailer for a heavy lunch. Tim insisted that she eat a complete steak, even though she was not hungry. By one o'clock he had taken the most precious of his scientific records out to the sled, and they were ready to go.

He tested the sled and its load a couple more times, then scanned the horizon to their south with his binoculars. 'There it goes!' he told her with a satisfied grin on his face. He handed her the glasses and gestured to a point on the horizon which seemed a tiny bit darker than the surrounding area. As she watched a pair of tiny red and green lights began to blink at her.

'It's there,' she shouted with glee. 'It's really there!'

He chuckled at her new-found enthusiasm. 'Oh ye of little faith! Come on. He's waiting for us.' He showed her how to slip the harness over her shoulders, and how to strap the X-shaped crampons on the bottom of her boots. Side by side they moved over the surface of the island, with the sled gliding smoothly behind them. 'My feet are sticking to the ice when the sharp points of these crampons sink in,' she complained.

'We'll need that extra traction when we go down the side of the island,' he assured her. 'Now, mush!'

'They don't say that in Greenland,' she warned him. 'But—oh my!'

They had come to the higher end of the island, and she could look down to the darker sea ice below. 'That must be fifty or sixty feet down,' she half whispered. 'Why don't we go to the other side of the island. It must be lower.'

'It is,' he assured her. 'But at the other side the island wall is tilted upward, and we would have a straight drop down. Here the wall of the island goes down at an angle, and we could almost walk down it. We have two choices. I can put a line around you and lower you, or we can rapell down the side. Didn't they teach you that in Basic Training?'

'Rapell! Oh, that. Yes, they did. We didn't have any mountains in central Texas, so we practised climbing down the side of the hospital building. Four storeys.' He had walked back to the sled before she added her final comment in an undertone. 'And I hated every minute of it!'

'Well,' he said, all cheery and enthusiastic. 'Since we both know the drill, you rapell down first. Then I'll lower the sled to you, and come down myself. Sound okay?'

'I—' But her pride refused to let her confess. 'Yes, of course. Okay.' He didn't seem to notice the squeak in her voice.

Together they uncoiled the ropes to estimate length. Then he took out a two-foot metal stake, and began driving it into the ice. When the first stake was deep, he drove another a few feet behind it. Then he carefully clipped the rope to both stakes and dropped its end over the edge. It touched sea ice with more than twenty feet to spare. He helped her into a heavy web belt with a shining D-ring attached.

'Now. Small jumps,' he reminded her. 'Your left hand on the rope, then it goes around the shoulder and the small of your back, and through the D-ring. As it comes out of the ring you bend it over, and hold it with your right hand. Remember, your right hand is the brake. When you pull the rope back against the D-ring, it stops running through. And don't get the spike on your crampons embedded too deeply. Set?'

She wound the rope around her, testing it by leaning back against it while still on the flat surface. Then she readjusted her face-mask, leaned outward against the rope, and stepped off the edge. Her first five-foot jump went easily, her feet coming back against the slope of the island, and the penetration of the crampons giving her enough purchase to jump again. She reached ocean-level without incident. It was only when she had unhooked and looked back at the towering height above her that she felt the reaction in the pit of her stomach. She waved an okay to him, almost out of sight, and stood back as the loaded sled began its precarious ride down the slope. She guided it for the last few feet, unfastened the ropes, and tugged it out of the way. Within minutes he, too, had rapelled down the cliff, in giant ten-foot steps, and stood at her side.

'There!' he exclaimed in exhilaration. 'That wasn't bad, was it? We're both arctic experts. It's about two-thirty now. Let's move off for a little bit, then camp for the night.'

Wordless, she shouldered her share of the sled harness, put her strength to the first few seconds which saw the sled begin to move, and plodded along beside him. Their first slow movements took them across a smooth patch of dark blue ice, the reformed pack-ice that had been broken up by the crashing drive of the ice island. But no sooner were they across this easy section, then they ran into the rolling ice hills of pressure ridges, set squarely across the path.

It took more than two hours before they managed to penetrate the barrier of the ridge-ice, and come down once again to fairly level snow-covered ice, dotted here and there by the towering heights of summer bergs, caught in position by the winter freeze.

She was totally exhausted, worn beyond the level of tiredness. Her shoulder, where the sled harness rested, was raw. In the heat she had pulled off her face-mask and pushed her hood back on her head. 'Tim?' she pleaded. He looked at her face and asked no questions.

'Over here,' he directed. They tugged the sled into the enclosing half-circle of one of the bergs. 'We'll stop for the night here,' he told her, helping her out of the harness. 'You sit down on the sled until I get things ready.'

As she watched he unpacked the separate panels of the igloo-shaped tent, and set it up. Then he zipped in the canvas floor, tossed the extra furs down to make a base, and lighted the tiny lamp hanging from a gimbal in the middle of the tent. Even with the light on inside, the colour of the outer tent wall blended almost exactly with the grey-white sides of the berg, rendering the tent almost invisible.

He pushed the sled around the other side of the berg, and came back to join her. The sun had, by now, swung all the way around to the south-west quadrant, and was losing its battle with a long line of heavy clouds which clung to the southern horizon. Their world stood in hushed twilight, although the white peaks of snow to their east still sparkled with rainbow sun-splinters. The ice beneath their feet turned from grey to dark blue. They stood side by side, his arm around her shoulders, looking into the pocket of distance where a set of red and white blinking lights gave them the illusion of safety and the promise of security.

'In you go,' he urged her. 'Duck into the bedroll, and we'll make what rest we can.' She stumbled ahead of him through the heavy zipper-opening that was the tent's door. Inside there was already a faint warmth to the air. She was barely able to stand up in the centre of the tent, and Tim, who followed her, had no chance at all. He went down on his knees to one edge of the bedroll, where he stored the radio, the flare gun, and an ice-pick.

'Okay, girl,' he ordered. 'Old army rule. Never stand up when you can sit down. Never sit down when you can lie down. Into the bedroll. Take off everything but your thermals—and if you get really warm during the night, take those off, too.'

'I—couldn't we put out the light?' she stammered.

'No, we can't,' he snorted. 'Come on now, you spent the night in an Inuit village. You know the procedure. That thing isn't a light, it's a heater. The tent is triple-walled. And if we keep it sealed up, we'll be as warm as we need to be in a couple of hours. What's the matter, Terry? Modesty?'

'Well—I didn't know what to expect. Yes, damn it, I'm embarrassed. I'm tired, and here we are, camped on a piece of ice in the middle of the ocean, and there's only one sleeping bag, and—'

And she was so tired that she could not stem the tears of frustration. 'All right, all right,' he said. 'I'll turn my back if that will make you feel better.' He did so, working on his mucklucs as if he hadn't a care in the world. Terry watched him warily for a moment, then skinned out of her clothes as fast as she could. She made her parka and snowtrousers up into a pillow, and slid into the sleeping bag with a sigh of relief. Moments later he joined her. She turned on her side to look at him, and her fingers accidentally brushed against his bare chest. She drew back as if she had touched a hot stove, and huddled as far from him as she could.

Whatever the adventure meant to him, he dropped off to sleep almost as soon as his head hit the pillow. She lay awake, pleased now to be able to watch him, her arms tucked under the back of her head. She was growing drowsily warmer, but before she slept this night she meant to do one more thing. She inspected his face carefully. His eyes were closed and his breathing was regular and quiet. Not fully trusting him, her fingers touched gently on his wrist and checked his pulse. As she did so he turned, and her hand slid to the bare warmth of his hip. She left it there, hoping not to disturb him. There was no further movement. Slowly, she withdrew her hand, unbuttoned her thermal underwear, and stripped it off. Then she moved close to him, huddled herself against the curve of his back, and, with one hand on his hip, she drifted off to sleep.

Something woke her up in the early morning hours. She was not sure whether it was a noise, or a movement, or a premonition. She stirred, noticed that the bright sunshine outside was illuminating the interior of the tent, and consulted her watch. It was three o'clock in the morning. The noise repeated itself from outside. A heavy chuffing sound, coupled with a low-pitched growl. She started to sit up, only to find herself caught and held in Tim's arms, unable to move. She struggled, opened her mouth to complain, and found his hand sealing her lips. He pulled her over until his mouth found her ear.

The outside noise had risen to a clatter, a smashing sound as if a heavy hand was investigating the load on the sled.

'Bear!' he whispered into her ear. 'Don't move. Don't make a sound.'

The smashing continued, accompanied by a few grunts of satisfaction. One final crash, and then there was silence. He released the pressure over her lips, but kept one warning finger in place. After fifteen of the longest minutes in her life, Terry felt Tim slip into his clothes without leaving the warmth of the bedroll, and cautiously unzipped the sealed door of the tent. He paused, searching, then wiggled out of her view on his stomach. Terry had sat up when he left, and the cold finally penetrated her conscious levels. She slid back down into the bedroll and waited.

It was another fifteen minutes before he returned, brushing snow off the front of his parka as he zipped up the tent again. 'Polar bear,' he said softly. 'Luckily we were upwind of him. He can't see worth a nickle, but his nose is too accurate for comfort. He got all the food supplies, except for a few sticks of beef jerky. Most of the rest of the stuff has been torn to pieces. The rifle's a wreck. We'd better lie doggo for a while. His tracks led out towards the open sea, but we don't want to be too close to him. Movement he can see. Put your head down, and try for a little more rest.'

He started to shed his clothes, and she ducked under the flap of the bedroll. Sure, put your head down. There's a polar bear out there somewhere, hunting. I'm lying on an ice-cube in a canvas tent. And inside with me there's a hungry bear. Hunting? She giggled, and before she could further analyse the world, sleep caught up with her and shut it off.

He stripped, groped his way into the bedroll beside her, and cautiously lay his arm over the warm flat muscles of her stomach. He moved closer, his heavy hand dropping over the sharp protruding bones of her rib-cage. Gradually his hand crept upward, until it rested precariously on her breast. She stirred, smiled, and from deep in her sleep murmured, 'Joshua?'

His hand snapped away from her breast. Stiffly he moved to the farthest limit of the bag. She stirred restlessly, turned on her side towards him, and followed. When her breasts bumped up against the hard wall of his chest she smiled in her sleep again. 'Joshua!' she repeated with a satisfied sigh, and fell quiet again.

When she awoke again, she could see the brilliant light of an arctic morning all around her. Her watch marked the eighth hour. As she wiggled to see the watch, her movements awakened him. He always woke up that way, she remembered. One moment he was deep in sleep, the next his eyes snapped wide, and he was fully conscious, ready for the world. She used one finger to push the cowlick back from his eyes, and then traced her finger down to his lips. But there was no response from him, and his eyes were cold, like gun-metal—dull, unresponsive.

She could feel the stab of pain deep in her heart. There was a comfort, a home-feeling, in his simple actions. And a coldness that overwhelmed all her strength. Good and evil, his body language seemed to tell her. He loves—and hates. She drew away from him, as far as the bedroll would allow.

'We've got to get going,' he told her. 'We've done four—five miles already. And we've got ten to go on this lovely winter day. Up and away, please.'

Impersonal, as if she were a stranger who just happened to be in the vicinity. Self-conscious, she dressed slowly in front of those all-seeing, uncaring eyes. She crammed herself back into each layer of clothing, watching out of the corner of her eyes as he did the same. The fears that had haunted her were back. She started to crawl out of the tent, but he stopped her.

'Man the hunter,' he said solemnly. 'Me first, you second. God only knows what might be waiting for us out there. You'd make a tasty breakfast.' He clicked a round into the firing chamber of the flare gun, and unzipped the flap. Terry scrambled out right behind him, slipping on the snow-glasses to protect herself from the glare. He led her around the berg to the sled, checking the snow as he went. Even to her untrained eye the track of the bear seemed enormous. Everything that they had left on the sled the night before was scattered over the ice, ripped to pieces. The sled itself had been battered. The aluminum frame and siderails had been dented and twisted, and only the steel runners retained their shape. Tim fumbled around among the remnants scattered on the ice and came up with a small cardboard box. He was shaking his head in disgust as he came back to her, but he made a visible effort to look happier when he arrived.

'Well, at least we've been saved one decision,' he said. 'Today we don't pull the sled. Right?'

'I—I guess not,' she stammered.

'Hungry?'

'Yes, Tim. I think I could eat that darn bear if he came back this way!'

'Poor child. Here, try this. He handed her what looked to be a long black stick of liquorice. 'Our little visitor wrecked everything in sight,' he added. 'All my instrumentation records are gone—even the water. But we've got enough jerky to last a few days. Eat up.'

'You've got to be kidding,' she snorted. 'This thing is frozen stiff.'

'It's all you're going to get until we reach land,' he commented. 'That's an adaptation of an old American Indian treat. It's dried smoked beef that's been pounded and stretched until all the sinews in it are broken down. Break off a little piece and let it melt in your mouth. As it unfreezes you'll get all the liquid you need. Then chew the remainder, and you'll get all the energy food you need. Carry the stick with you today, and every half an hour or so nibble on another piece.'

She tried it out while he surveyed the rest of their goods. To her surprise the meat, when melted, was both chewy and tasty. There was a flavour beyond the beef. Blueberries? She marvelled at her own imagination, but when he returned he assured her it was no accident.

'They pound blueberries into it when it's been smoked,' he said. 'But I can't see those beacon lights. Sit tight.' He went over to the mini-berg that had been their shelter for the night, and made his way up the convex side, until he was a good thirty feet above the sea ice. She watched him anxiously. He scanned the horizon in a great circle, stood on his perch, immobile for a moment, then slid and skidded down to her level.

He threw back his hood as he came up to her. She could see the frown on his face, the lines of care that ran outwards from his eyes towards his ears. She started to say something, but he held up his hand.

'Keep your voice down,' he whispered. 'The beacon lights are straight ahead of us. We're closer than I thought. And the bear is just on the other side of that pressure ridge—and *he's* closer than I thought. We're still down-wind of him. At that distance he won't be able to see us—but he has good ears. Let's move!'

The going was easier without the sled behind them. At the first halt he had her sit down, and he unstrapped the crampons from her boots. 'You won't need these any more,' he said. 'It looks like clear sailing for the rest of the trip.' She peered ahead, shading her eyes. There, dead ahead, just showing over the top of another pressure ridge, she could see the blinking lights!

He reached into his pocket and pulled out the little radio. Still almost whispering he repeated his call into the microphone, and waited. Eventually a tinny voice responded. She was only half hearing, her mind a thousand thoughts away, but she did hear the last phrase, just before he snapped the antenna down. 'There's a bear trailing us,' he reported. 'He's definitely following our trail. We've got to move fast.' And then he put the radio away, pulled her to her feet, and

started on the trek again. But she had to tell him. She lagged
back against his urging, and he stopped and looked at her.

'Tim? I—I have to say something to you. Now. I wish I
knew all the words for what I—I. I wish, Tim, that I could
know you now instead of knowing you then. I—you're a
wonderful man, Tim Alden. The me that knows you now
likes you very much. Am I making much sense?'

'Does this mean that you're not afraid of me any more?'
He spoke softly, with a controlled sense of urgency, and a
certain coldness behind it all.

'I'm not sure of that. I think I'm still afraid. I don't
know, really. I feel as if you and I have stood at the end of
the world—at the end of existence—and have comforted
each other. Am I assuming too much? You needn't answer
if you don't want to.'

'I think we should push on, Teresa,' he said in a monotone. 'We have a great deal we should talk about, but not in
the middle of the ocean.'

'Okay,' she returned, in a quiet subdued voice. By giving
no answer he had answered her. She had brought herself to
the brink, mustered all her courage, for one statement of
commitment, and he had drawn back. There were two tiny
tears in her eyes as she bent forward and began the gliding,
sliding motion that ice-walking required.

The bright sun was flashing rainbows across the ice-world
in which they were immersed, and had pushed happiness
into the farthest corner of her soul. She concentrated on her
feet. Lift one, slide it forward, lift the other, slide. The lit-
any of the movement dulled her perceptions. She became an
automaton stalking across the sea ice in a mindless hunt for
emotional extinction, freezing her heart against the world
that had hurt her too many times before. She hardly noticed it when he brought her to a stop, and pulled her body
back to see her face.

'Time for a break,' he said. 'You haven't been eating the
way I told you. Take another piece of jerky.'

'Yes,' she muttered. She broke off a small piece of the strange food, lifted her face-mask, and put it in her mouth.

'Are you feeling all right?' he asked anxiously. She had slumped down on a chunk of frozen snow, barely able to control her knee muscles.

She shook her head, too miserable to make an answer.

'We've come more than halfway,' he said, cracking one of his own food-sticks and greedily sucking on it. 'It can't be more than two or three miles to go. Shall we push on? Say something, Teresa!'

'I'm—I'm sure you're right,' she said quietly, trying to hide her mental distress behind a mask of formality. 'I'm ready to go on when you are.'

Instead of moving on, he came over to where she was sitting, and brushed her face-mask aside. He slipped off his heavy gloves and prodded at her chin with two fingers, lifting her head so that she was forced to stare into his eyes. She could not disguise the misery. He looked hard at her, then pulled her face-mask down, and sighed.

'All right, Terry,' he said. 'Let's push on.'

CHAPTER NINE

THEIR SECOND DAY on the ice was the same in form as the first, but completely different in attitude. He had made two small backpacks out of the bedroll, the food, and a couple of the usable furs. They shuffled forward for the first two hours at almost running speed, making two wide detours to find easier places to cross the ice-ridges that blocked their path. He essayed conversation twice, but she was too miserable to respond. He gave up the attempt, and they went forward until the sun stood directly in front of them, to the south, and his watch read noon.

'Stop here,' he ordered. She dropped to the ice at his first word, too tired to comment. He continued on for a few paces, looking for a higher vantage point. The winking lights of the Weather Station seemed to be straight ahead of them, at the end of a long narrow path of clear ice. By the time he came back she had struggled to a sitting position, using one of her sweaters for a cushion.

'Are you okay?' he asked.

'Sure,' she returned in a flat monotone. He shrugged his shoulders and squatted down beside her. She flinched away from him.

'Like that, huh?'

'Yes. Like that.'

'And just when I thought we were getting somewhere.'

'Just when you thought *you* were getting somewhere. I'm not planning any side trips.'

He spread out the bedroll on the ice and smoothed it down. 'Settle on that,' he suggested. 'We did well this morning. I think we must be less than a mile from land. Maybe a mile and a half from the station.'

'That's nice.' There was such a hard ball of misery in her stomach that she could not help but show it. She not only sounded sarcastic, but looked it, too. She moved over and stretched out on top of the bedroll. He spread the remaining furs over her.

'I see,' he said. 'You're not really interested in getting there, is that it?'

'No, that's not it!' she snapped. 'I'm immensely interested in getting there, and the sooner the better. I wish—'

'You wish what?'

'I wish I had never come to Greenland!' And the dam broke, flushing tears down her face in a torrent of woe.

'Hey now.' He tried to comfort her, but she would have no part of it. Or him. She turned her back on him and curled as far away as she could get from him without falling on to the ice. If I live through this, she told herself, I'll run so far that—if I live through this! The thought sent shudders up and down her spine. Was there really anything else to do? I've run to the end of the earth, and it's not far enough. But I'm not going to let him drive me off the edge! Which left only one other course to take. Stand up to him. Defy him! Damn him to do whatever he wanted, and go down with all flags flying! All the thousands of years of her Portuguese ancestry came flooding to her rescue. War—outright war— against the Romans, the Goths, the Moslems, the Spaniards, the Aldens! It was so ridiculous an idea that she giggled through her tears, set her stubborn little chin, and fell into a deep sleep. Throughout her dream she saw the fully armoured maiden, Saint Teresa of New Bedford, striding up the ramparts of Hawthorne Street to successfully storm the Alden Castle, and put her dainty size six shoe on the neck of the defeated villain, Sir Timothy the Blackhearted. It was a very enjoyable dream. Had she known that her continued giggles kept him awake, she might have enjoyed it even better.

At two o'clock he prodded her awake. Her first sensation was a groan. 'My legs,' she gasped. 'I can't move them!'

'Yeah, I know.' He dived down into the furs and began gently to massage her leg muscles back into co-operative form. It took five minutes. 'That better?' he asked.

'Much,' she admitted grudgingly. 'Thank you.'

'I've heard more enthusiastic thanks,' he commented.

'I don't doubt it,' she snarled at him. 'I ache in every bone and muscle. I've been sleeping on ice. And all I need to make my day complete is a wise guy!'

'Okay, okay,' he answered. 'You never used to be a wake-up grouch!'

'How would you know,' she started to say. 'You never stayed around long enough—' Her hand flew up to her mouth and applied a quick tourniquet on her babbling tongue. 'I'm sorry, Tim. I should never have said that. It wasn't even true.'

'It's all right. I'm not a ball of sunshine myself. Can you get moving?' She nodded, and proceeded to do so. She passed up and down for the few minutes that it took him to re-pack the bedroll and furs. There was a ruthless efficiency about him when he worked, she noticed. Things seemed to flow into place at his touch. She could remember his clumsy eagerness when they had first met. Even before they were married going out with him had been a form of adventure, never knowing when, by accident, his massive hands would squeeze too tight, and bruise her. Or the Senior Prom, when one of his feet had tripped her on the dance floor, and sent her sprawling down the floor in her first full-length gown. All changed. She picked up her share of the pack, and started off.

'Don't forget to eat!' he yelled across at her.

'Eat!' she groaned, but nevertheless pulled the stick of jerky from her pocket, broke off a piece, and sucked on it. With the sun out continuously it was growing warmer. She slipped back her hood and pulled off her face-mask. A few hundred yards ahead of them she could see the loose snow being blown up in tiny whirlwinds as the surface breeze eddied and grew in strength. She lowered her head and struggled on. When he moved closer to her and spoke, his voice was so soft that she almost missed his command. 'Stop! Freeze right where you are!' he repeated softly. Instant fear ground her to a halt. She raised her head and looked vaguely around, re-focusing on the trail behind them.

'What is it?' she whispered, and then realising the idiocy of trying to communicate by whispers, said in a normal tone, 'What's the matter?'

'Just be quiet,' he commanded. 'Don't move. That damn bear is right behind us, and he's got a friend. He may not be able to see us if we don't move.'

Slowly he pushed her down to the ice and followed her, eyes glued to the northward, behind them. 'All right,' he muttered in her ear. 'They're wandering away from the trail. There's a small berg off to our right. As slowly as you can, wiggle over there—on your stomach!' She followed his instructions in petrified detail. He joined her, pushing her hard up against the far side of the little berg.

'I think it must be the same bear that hit us last night,' he told her. 'With friend. Let's hope he's found a seal's blow-hole, instead of us. Sit quietly.'

'Like a church mouse!' she promised him. It was not just the temperature that was making her knees knock. She found herself wishing she had been more attentive on Sundays in church. The prayers she managed to scrabble up seemed hardly strong enough to fit the requirement.

'They've split up,' he whispered to her. 'One of them has cut out like an express train towards the west. The other one is looking straight at us!'

'I can't stand much of this,' she whispered back. 'I'm almost petrified, Tim. How can you be so cool?'

'It isn't hard,' he commented. 'The temperature is only ten above zero.'

'It doesn't help to joke about it,' she accused him. 'He's coming this way!' She stuffed her mouth with one of her gloves to stifle her scream. 'I can't help it, Tim! I'm coming apart at the seams! I just can't sit here and watch him come at us. We've got to do something, Tim. Please!'

'Yes. You're right. Don't get over-excited.' He rose from his crouch to a kneel position, and surveyed the area carefully.

'God, I wish we had the rifle,' he said. 'How stupid could I get, leaving our only rifle outside on the sled. Well. Look, Terry.' He gestured towards the south. 'It's almost clear ice from here to the land. Except for that pile of snow down there. You see it?'

She clung to his arm, followed the direction of his pointing finger, and nodded. 'That bear isn't really close enough to see us,' he continued, 'and we're still downwind from him. I'm going to try to distract him. Now, you hear me real good, girl. I want you to do exactly what I tell you, and no arguments. Understand?'

'Of course I'll do what you say, but I don't understand!'

'No more time. Just do it. When I tap you on the shoulder you count up to twenty. When you get to twenty, get up and run like hell for the land. And keep going, no matter what happens!'

'I—yes, Tim!'

'No more time. Start counting. Now!' She fell to the ice as he jumped up. With eyes closed she counted. He stood up, yelled a wild Comanche yell at the bear, and ran directly into its path, waving the flare gun over his head. Frightened completely out of her wits, Terry completed the count, then blindly started to run for the shore. Behind her she could hear Tim still yelling at the top of his lungs.

Halfway to the large patch of snow it suddenly struck her just what he was doing. He was distracting the bear, presenting himself as a target, so that she could escape! She stopped and whirled around.

'No, Tim!' she screamed. 'You can't do that! You can't, Tim! Let it come for me!' But she could see that it was already too late. The bear, confronted by the charging and shouting man, had stretched up to his full ten-foot height, and was ready to do battle. With one last shout, Tim stopped, aimed the flare gun, and sent a burning flame straight at the side of the growling monster.

The bear backed away, afraid of the fire, and pawed the burning projectile aside. But because it represented the closer danger, the bear turned to guard against it. The flare, its fuse lit, but its bomb not yet exploded, rolled around in little circles on the ice just a few feet to the left of the bear's paw.

'Run, Terry!' Tim shouted. She was conditioned to obey. She got up from where she had fallen and staggered onwards, just as the flare exploded. The bear roared a challenge, but backed off from the ball of burning light. Tim was running behind her. She could hear the clump of his footsteps. She dug in her heels and ran, but already the bear had skirted the flare and taken up pursuit of the easier targets. His lazy loping run brought him down on them with the speed of a freight train.

As Terry flashed by the pile of snow she knew that she was running a losing race, and that the prize for losing would be death. The bear was only twenty paces behind Tim, gaining on every stride. And then she noticed something else out of the corner of her eye. The snow-pile was not really snow at all! It was a white canvas screen, and behind it, flat on the ice, lay a human figure with hands on the largest rifle she had ever seen. As she staggered to an astonished halt a thunderous boom, almost like a cannon shot, came from behind the screen. The bear staggered as the first fifty-calibre slug hit him in the shoulder, he had taken two more paces when the second splattered into his skull, and was already dead when the third shot sent him spinning down to the ice. But Terry, who could only vaguely see the figure of man and bear, counted the shots, lost her balance, and slid forward on to the ice on stomach and outstretched hands, like Lou Brock stealing second base, and fainted.

As she struggled back from the swamps of blackness, she could not recall exactly what had happened. She was stretched out on a moving vehicle of some sort, bumping over the worst back road in New Jersey. She moaned an appeal, and the movement stopped instantly. Terry managed to pry one eye open. She was looking directly into a wide, cheerful smile on a wind-creased bronze face. 'Charlie!' she exclaimed. 'What are you doing here!'

The Inuit grinned even wider. 'You remember me? I come to turn on the lights and shoot the bear!' he laughed. 'Did you see me shoot the bear? Bang! Wham! And old man bear falls down dead just like that! Did you see?' He was so excited that he was doing a little primitive dance along the edge of the sled that was carrying her. 'Now you see!' he continued, breaking into a chant. 'I am called Ungarlak, the seal-hunter. Never have I shot the seal. Today I am Kills-the-Bear! Hear me, Sun-Woman?' He was shouting straight up into the sky, dancing.

'That's great,' she cheered him weakly. 'But where's Tim? I saw the bear hit him. Where's Tim?'

'Right over here.' The voice came from the other side of the sled. She turned her head, wincing at the pain. He had knelt down beside her in the snow, his strong craggy face inches away from hers.

'I saw the bear hit you!' she whispered. 'I saw it!'

'No you didn't, Teresa Alden,' he said. 'We all know that you're blind as a bat at over fifty feet. He didn't come within ten feet of me.'

'But—but you did that for me! Just for me! Did you know Charlie was there with the gun? Did you?'

'No, that was a surprise, I admit it. Now don't start on that hero-worship stuff, Terry. We don't need that. I figured that fire would scare the animal off, and then I got so scared that I ran in the wrong direction.'

'You lie, Tim. Kiss me!' She pulled his head down and caressed his lips gently. He stiffened momentarily, then sighed and relaxed in the enjoyment of the simple contact.

'Hey, we got two hours, maybe, to supper,' Charlie interrupted them. 'You think it's nice to make out on ice? You gotta remember this big bushwhacker here has got him a mate running around somewhere on the ice. Me, I prefer we go up to the house, and watch through the window when Mamma comes along looking for her boyfriend!'

'Where are we?' Terry inquired, sitting up on the sled. The moment she moved she wished that she hadn't. The front of her head hurt. Her hand explored the newly formed bump.

'Yeah, you did it again,' Tim assured her. 'You're the damnedest woman for cracking your skull. I'm surprised that the brains haven't all leaked out!'

'I think they did. Some years ago,' she returned. 'Where are we?'

'If you was to take four steps forward,' Charlie told her, 'your foot is on Foot Peninsula. Four steps.'

'That's a funny name. Foot Peninsula?'

'Sure. Old Inuit custom, to name the land after pieces of the body, you know. Many years ago, a small family comes here, and they name the Peninsula *Foot* and the Mountain *Heart*.'

'What mountain?' She sat up again and looked in the direction he was pointing. 'That's a mountain? It wouldn't rate as a low-grade hill, even in Holland.'

'When we before went to Etah, I told you,' Charlie reminded her. 'Inuit people like to make jokes. Story says that father of this family have big foot, small heart. So they name the mountains and the peninsula, and everybody remembers. But not his name. Only the Woman of the Sea knows his name. And she never tells. So, we go?'

'Yeah, we go, Nanook of the North,' Tim chipped in. 'You stay on the sled, Terry. We'll pull.'

'Crazy white man,' Charlie muttered as he slipped into the harness on his side of the sled. 'I never heard of this Nanook guy. He plays for the Yankees?'

'Just pull,' Tim laughed. 'Just pull. Why is the white man crazy?'

'Look in back of you,' Charlie shouted. 'Two men pull the sled, like a dog team, huh? Woman rides. Any real Inuit woman would know to pull the sled herself, and let the man ride. Only way to go. What you say to that, crazy white man?'

'What I say is that we're running out of snow, and this darn sled won't slide over these rocks. Now what?'

'Now we pick up the sled and carry it,' Charlie responded. 'Very simple, huh?'

'Simple is right,' Terry interjected. 'At this point the woman gets off and walks. This sled and equipment are worth about fifty dollars, I would guess. And the house is a half-mile up there?' Both the men nodded.

'So we leave the whole thing here, and together we three stroll the distance and get inside the house before the snow starts. Not many thieves up in this area, are there?'

'That's true, but there is another polar bear.' Tim pulled off his face-mask so that she could see the smile on his face.

'Woman speaks with straight tongue!' Charlie interjected.

'Damn! You see too many Wild West movies.' Tim laughed at him, and Charlie had the gall to laugh back.

'Next thing I do is Lone Ranger and Tonto,' the Inuit added. 'So we walk. After you, madame.'

The bump on her forehead ached, but she inched to her feet, patted the sled they were abandoning, and started off up the pebble-covered hill toward the foot of Heart Mountain. A cluster of four little wood and sod and stone houses huddled against the hill, with only the slanted eaves of the roof, and the red paint almost covering the outside, to distinguish them from an Inuit settlement. Until she got closer, that was. The sparkle that struck her eyes could be only one thing—a house with windows! She stopped to admire, the men waiting patiently behind her. A tiny trickle of steam made a ladder from the chimney on one of the houses up to the rapidly clouding sky, and a tall thin radio tower crowned the top of the hill. She smiled at the homeliness of it, and moved off again.

The walk required concentration. The stones under their feet were loose, and liable to roll at the slightest provocation. All three kept their heads down as they walked. Snow was squirting at them by the time they reached the front door, and squall winds were starting their high-pitched whine through the guy wires of the antenna.

'Electricity?' Terry asked as she stepped into the lighted interior of the house.

'Here?' Charlie guffawed. 'Not a chance, lady. Oil lamps, steam radiators, coal heat.'

'Coal?'

'Sure. That's why they built the station here. There's a vein of coal in the mountain in back of us. A few weeks of work in the summer provides enough coal to last all year. We must have five to six tons left out there in the coal shed. And enough kerosine for two or three years. Plus a one-year supply of canned food. How about that!'

'Well now, if you're about to tell me that there's hot and cold running water, I'll be happy—delirious!'

'We've saved you, then,' Tim interjected. 'Water yes. Melted snow in the wintertime, like now, and a lake out back in the summer.'

'Lord, what I'd give for a hot shower,' she mourned.

'White man custom,' Charlie chuckled. 'Better to go without. Put bear grease all over, wash once in summer—that's the way to do it!'

'I don't care,' she responded, dropping into a homemade easy chair by the rickety box-table. 'I'm home! There's a real roof over my head, and windows to look out, and—beds?'

Tim stomped back into the room, a broad smile on his face. 'Been exploring,' he reported. 'Two bedrooms, kitchen, radio room, bathroom, and this lounge. All steam heated from that boiler building over there. Nice and warm. How's your head feel, Terry?'

'My head's all right—if I don't move it too fast. But the rest of me feels like a raw potato.'

'There's a bath tub in there. We could heat you some water on the kitchen stove. Want it?'

It took the combined effort of both men to bring enough water to provide three inches in the tub, and by that time the water had become tepid. She smiled her thanks, shut the door firmly behind them, and stripped everything off. The sheer relief at being able to stand and stretch, naked, was a pleasant surprise. She climbed into the tiny tub and relaxed, like a deflating balloon. She kept her hands at work, splashing the water up over the rest of her, then lathered up and scrubbed every inch twice. She was still vigorously engaged in the scrubbing when the door opened. She snatched up her towel and held it over her breast, too angry to do more.

'What in the world are you doing in here,' she shouted at him.

'I'm trying to be helpful,' Tim said sarcastically. 'I found this for you to wear.' He held out a fairly respectable terry-cloth robe. 'And these.' He offered a pair of sponge-rubber clogs. 'The floors seem to be pretty cold.'

'Thank you,' she snapped. 'Now will you get out of here!'

'You look lovely,' he responded. 'And for a girl who's just completed her first arctic trek, that's saying a lot.'

'Yes? Get out of here,' she ordered. He shrugged his shoulders and walked out. The interruption had spoiled the mood of her bathtime. She climbed out of the tub, dried herself carefully, made liberal use of a can of powder left on the shelf, and put on the robe.

Tim was standing alone by one of the windows, watching something outside. She went over to join him.

'What is it?' she asked.

'It's that crazy Eskimo. Look at him.'

'He doesn't like to be called Eskimo. What's he doing?'

'He's so tickled about killing that bear that he's gone back to get the paws for a trophy. And then he says he's going to go off by himself and really hunt down a seal. Crazy!'

'I don't see anything crazy about it,' she said primly. 'It's his lifetime ambition. Only I'm afraid—well, the weather is changing again, isn't it?'

'He'll do very well with any kind of weather. This is his environment, remember. Besides, he's taking that crazy elephant gun with him. Says he won it in a poker game with an English hunter. If he shoots a seal with that cannon there won't be anything left to stuff!'

'He'll be gone for—' It wasn't the poor Inuit, out in the snow and storm that she was worried about. She bit her lip to hide her vexation.

'About three or four days.'

'You mean we'll be alone here for three or four days?'

'Sure. What's eating you, Terry? We were alone on the ice island. What's the problem?'

'That was different!'

'How different?'

'I—I don't know. It was just different, that's all. Out there we were just existing. Here we're in a house, with furniture, and windows, and—it's just different!'

'I don't see it, Teresa. The difference, I mean.'

'Well I do. I don't want to be alone with you here. Which bedroom do you want?'

'The one you want, of course.'

'No! There'll be nothing like that. I told you, I don't want to be alone with you!'

'You also told me, out there on the ice, that you liked me a lot. Change your mind? You weren't too hard to get along with the night the island broke up, either, were you.'

'That was—different!'

'Different! Can't you get that word out of your vocabulary for a while? That night on the island, you thought we were both going to die, didn't you, and you *wanted* to share your pure white body with me. Wasn't that it?'

'I—I don't want to talk about it. I don't want to talk to you at all. Why can't you just keep out of my way until the helicopters come?'

'I don't think I can do that, Terry, but I'll try as best I can.'

She stormed out of the room before he could add another word. Her anger blunted her senses. She found herself in one of the bedrooms, hands twisted tightly behind her, so tightly that her nails were scratching her palms. She looked, unseeing, out of the window, where the snowflakes had begun to make a serious effort. All the little joys, the little happiness she had felt on the island and on the trek, had faded the moment they stepped in to what she recognised as a real house. The name, the term, brought back to her all the strictures of her upbringing, all the fears and foibles of her years alone. She willed herself to move. There was a small oil lamp on the bedside table, and the gathering storm had darkened the room. She managed to light it, and looked around.

The tiny bedroom was furnished in Spartan fashion. The bed itself was of double-width, but obviously hand-built on site, from sturdy beams. A chest of drawers stood against the wall, made out of heavy corrugated paper. Two straight chairs provided cold comfort on the bare floor, and a single picture—a photograph of the canals in Venice—hung on the wall. She walked over to the bureau and opened the drawers. To her amazement the bottom two were full—of men's clothing, of course. But she had accustomed herself to that, and she actually bubbled with glee as she shucked off the robe and tied herself into a pair of trousers and a shirt. There were no neckties to use as straps this time, but she remembered that her braces were still in her discarded garments in the bathroom. Holding the trousers up with one hand, she sneaked out of the bedroom and into the bath. By the time she had made some major adjustments, the clothing was comfortable, if not stylish. Only one thing bothered her. She almost cried at the lack of underwear—something smooth and silky next to her skin, lace decorated, feminine. But not in Nyboesland! She returned to the bedroom with her discarded things, meaning to find some way to wash them in the morning.

When she came back out into the lounge the threatening storm had become a reality, and darkness was the order of the day. A lamp was burning merrily by the easy chair, and next to it was a newspaper. She sat down cautiously, not sure that her tailoring efforts would hold up. When they did, she leaned back and picked up the paper. She was halfway through the first section when she discovered that it was the Boston Globe of three years earlier. The revelation tickled her fancy, and she was laughing as Tim came into the room.

'Laughing?' he quipped. 'Was there a double axe murder in the paper?'

'No,' she clipped out, unwilling to share the joke.

'Terry, I need you,' he said bluntly, holding out his hand.

She half rose from the chair and glared at him. 'I don't care,' she snapped. 'I'm not going to let you use *me*! I'm not a reusable container, you know!'

'I didn't mean that, damn it,' he roared back at her. 'Is that the only rut your mind runs in these days? I need you—

in the radio room.' He turned and stalked out. With a blushing red face she followed.

The radio room looked much less crowded than the one on the ice island, and everything was quiet. 'What do you need me for?' she asked.

'I have a schedule to talk to Thule in ten minutes,' he replied. 'I need some electricity.'

'I thought we didn't have any electricity up here,' she argued stubbornly.

'We don't. Look over there.' 'Over there' was a sort of exercise bicycle, one half of a bicycle firmly fixed on a stand, with a seat, steering mechanism, chain, and pedals. But instead of a rear wheel, the chain was attached to a little motor.

'It's a generator,' he said quietly. 'It provides just enough power to run the radio, or the Met equipment. But somebody has to ride it to produce the power.'

'Ah! You expect me to sit on that thing and pedal while you sit back at your desk and talk?'

'Yup! Unless you'd prefer to talk to them yourself?'

She suddenly remembered her two fiascos with the small battery radio. 'No. No, thank you,' she muttered. 'I'll ride your bike. Now?'

He waved her to the seat. She climbed up, adjusting her feet to the pedals. When he called to her she began to pedal. It was a hard job at the start, but as she worked up to speed the load became easier, and she was able to pedal and listen. After he established contact a voice dictated to him a synoptic weather forecast. All she understood was the last part.

'And we expect this storm to be a cyclonic disturbance equal to the last one, and lasting approximately four days. With that delay added, it is probable that we will require two more weeks after the storm to establish the relay rescue station, and another two days to pick you up at your present site. The new storm will start in approximately three days

from now. The present snow in your area is only local, and
will blow out by 0400 tomorrow morning. In the mean time,
a C-130 will overfly your station tomorrow, on a routine
training flight. Is there anything that you need?'

Tim turned around to her. 'A further delay,' he told her.
'Another fifteen days, perhaps. What should they drop us?'

Before she could even think out the words she said,
'Please! Underwear. And some dresses. I'm sick to death of
wearing cast-off men's clothing. And some soap—some
perfumed soap. Please?'

He chuckled as he flipped the microphone switch. 'Thule
Airways, this is NASA 82,' he said. 'Advise possibility of
dropping wardrobe for female member. Pressing priority.
Also newspapers, books, pipe tobacco. Over.'

'Ah. NASA 82,' the voice from the speaker rumbled. 'We
acknowledge drop gown for Cinderella. Have heard much
here about the Ice Lady. The Base Commander sends her his
personal congratulations. Thule out.'

'Time we got something civilised to eat,' Tim told her
taking her arm gently and helping her to dismount. 'Ice
Lady! How appropriate.'

'I didn't invent the name,' she retorted haughtily. 'They
did. Ice Lady, indeed. You'd better think of something better than that to talk about if you aim to have conversation
with your dinner.'

'Oh, don't let that worry you,' he returned. 'We'll have
conversation with our dinner all right. For starters, you
could tell me all about Joshua!'

CHAPTER TEN

DESPITE HIS CONTINUAL and merciless probing, she managed to maintain a deadly silence for forty-eight hours. Her whole plan, her hold on sanity, was based on the idea that Charlie would be back soon. And with a third party witness, she might still be safe.

Twice she helped Tim make radio contact. Together they went out into the clearing sunshine of the second day, and recovered the material dropped by drogue-chutes from a low-flying C-130. When they had back-packed the miscellaneous packages back to the house, she disappeared into her bedroom and propped a chair backwards under the door knob. An hour later Tim knocked on the door. She opened for him, silently, and could see the laugh-lines around his mouth as he noted the chair being set aside. He handed her a battered flight bag.

'Your share of the loot,' he announced. 'They dropped us a week's supply of fresh steaks. Rather have that for supper instead of the canned hash and beans?'

She took the flight bag from him without a word, and waited impatiently for him to leave. He stalled, obviously hoping to tease her into saying something, but after a moment he chuckled and left. She slammed the door behind him, and pounced on the flight bag. Someone in Thule had raided her wardrobe indiscriminately. The bag contained six or seven days' supply of briefs and bras, as well as a long house-coat, three white dresses, two half-slips, and two pairs of shoes. Tucked into one corner of the bag was her cosmetic kit.

Terry unpacked slowly, savouring each item, like a child with a second Christmas in the same year. A little later, hearing Tim go into the radio room, she took a dress and a complete change of clothes to the bathroom. From the kitchen stove she ladled out a basin of hot water, and treated herself to a sponge bath. Dressing restored her courage. She lingered over simple things, the soft caress of silk as she slipped into her cerulean-coloured briefs, the swish of sound as she twirled in her lace-trimmed half-slip, the touch of soft leather as she slipped her foot into a real pair of shoes. And then she brushed her hair vigorously, and went out to the kitchen, where she prepared them both a dinner of steak, canned beans, and canned asparagus tips.

'They dropped us a pile of newspapers and books,' Tim said casually as they finished the dinner. 'You've made the headlines in the New York papers. How about this one: "Valiant Nurse Crashes in Arctic Drama. Story on page two." Want to read it?'

'I don't believe you. You've made it all up,' she snapped at him. 'Is it really?'

'No. I made it all up. I just wanted to hear another voice around here.'

'You can hear one easily. Charlie will be back tomorrow. Won't he?'

'Who knows what that madman will do? He's gone primitive. He thinks he's the reincarnation of his great-grandfather. A mighty hunter!'

'He's just trying to find himself. You shouldn't make fun of him like that. He's nice. Very nice. Goodnight.'

'Goodnight? It's only seven o'clock! You can't be all that sleepy!'

'I am. Is the storm still coming?'

'Be here late tomorrow. Should be a real zinger when it arrives.'

She looked at him curiously. 'You never used to talk like that.'

'I know. But I gave up the Spartan warrior a lot of years ago. I learned to speak what's on my mind, to cry when I'm hurt, to ache when I'm miserable—oh, a lot of things you don't know about.'

'I see,' she said non-committally. She got up and stacked the dishes in the sink, then picked up a share of the newspapers and started back to her room.

'You're leaving me the dishes?' he called after her.

'Yes,' she returned. 'I learned to give up "woman's work" and how to be happy by myself, and—oh, lots of things you don't know about.' She slammed her door behind her, propped the chair under the knob again, and went to bed.

She read until early in the following morning, propped up in bed with an ancient kerosine lamp at her side. But her concentration was poor. More than once she re-read a complete page, as she listened for his footsteps. Tim went into the radio room for a time, then into the bathroom. His steps halted outside her door at one time, and Terry froze, her fingers shaking the paper back and forth until it crackled. But after a couple of minutes she heard him pad off, and the door of the adjacent bedroom opened and closed.

The walls between the rooms were thin. She could hear him walk around, drop some metal items on his bureau, and eventually she heard the springs of his bed complain under his weight. Only then did she really start breathing. At about two-thirty in the morning the paper slipped from her fingers, and she dropped off to sleep with the lamp still burning.

It was the smell that woke her up. The lamp had flickered to the end of its small fuel supply, and then snuffed itself out, leaving the wick to smoke and to fill the room with the odour of burnt oil. It was eight o'clock, and bright sunlight glared through the window.

Hearing no noises from next door, she dressed quickly and went out to the kitchen for a cup of instant coffee. Charlie would be back today! And with his arrival the uneasy twosome would become a manageable threesome. But when would he arrive? Her resolve was weakening every minute she remained alone with Tim. Some drastic action was indicated. Her eye was caught by the glitter of light on the radio tower, plainly visible through the kitchen window. It was the sight of the lights on the tower that gave her the idea. She scribbled a quick 'I'm going out' on the pad of paper by the kitchen table, grabbed up her outdoor clothes and his binoculars, and went out into the cold.

The near summit of Heart Mountain beckoned to her. She fixed her hood and face-mask, and started the slow climb up the side of the hill. The mountainside was peculiar. From a little distance it looked almost like an abandoned Greek archaeological site. Little flat plateaux, glazed in slate, were surrounded by square pillars of stone, looking for a roof to hold up. But she knew better. It was all an illusion, brought about by the random carving of water flowing into little cracks, freezing, and expanding. The harder stone resisted, and left pillars; the softer stone cracked, was rolled into pebbles, and blew away.

She stopped halfway up to catch her breath, just as the low-level sun was obliterated by scudding storm clouds. She fumbled for the binoculars, and scanned the ocean to her north. She could barely see the remains of their ice island, perched precariously among the pigmy bergs of the sea. She struggled on.

There was a little hut on top of the mountain, at the base of the radio antenna. She ducked into its shelter wishing that she had thought to bring a lunch. Her hand, fumbling with her parka, felt a hard object in her pocket. She slipped off the gloves and explored, laughing when she brought out two broken sticks of jerky, her only memory of that mad dash across the sea ice. 'So eat, already,' she told herself, in mimic of *his* commands, and set action to words, sucking on two of the tiny segments as she explored briefly the other side of the mountain. 'And that certainly proves a point!' she laughed, as she reached a convenient stopping place. 'What is there on the other side of the mountain? More of the same!'

By two o'clock she was certain that Charlie had returned, and besides the clouds were gathering in dark choruses, spitting snow out on the sea ice. She hurried as best she could, back to the weather station. Just outside the house she came upon a sign that made her feel better. The large wooden rack, which had been empty when she left, now held the pegged-out skin of a polar bear. She quickened her step, and went into the house.

'Been taking the air?' Tim asked as she came into the living room.

'I—yes. The name intrigued me. Heart Mountain. I wanted to see what it's like. Where's Charlie?'

'I'll bet the mountain's as cold as some other hearts around this place, isn't it?'

'I—I don't want to play word games with you!' She fluffed out her hair to relieve it from the pressure of both the parka hood and her face-mask. As far as she could see, Charlie had disappeared. She asked again, a little more concerned than before. 'Where's Charlie?'

'Oh him? Were you waiting for him? He came in this morning and staked out his bearskin. Did you see what a monster that was?'

'Yes, I saw. But where's Charlie now?'

'Oh, now! Well, I told you he'd gone primitive, didn't I? He says he could smell the storm. He came in to leave his skin and to collect some food. He's built himself an igloo down the gulf a-ways. About fifteen miles away, I guess. Says he's going to wait the storm out down there. Says he's actually found a seal blow-hole, and he plans to camp out there until he can get him a seal.'

'But he can't do that!' Her voice rose an octave. 'He can't! He'll be—he'll be hurt or something! And how will he know when the rescue team comes?'

'Hey, don't get so excited. He won't be hurt. His people have been doing this sort of thing for years. His igloo will be just as strong as this house. Maybe stronger. And the rescue team will fly right over his head when they come. And if he misses that, we'll fire a rocket for him. Now, what other complaints do you have?'

'I—he—did he ask for me?' Terry stammered. She had drifted back to the far corner of the room, as far away from Tim as she could get, pressing her hip against the bookcase that stood against the wall.

'Oh yes. He asked for the Ice Lady. I told him you had gone off.'

'He knew the storm was coming! He wouldn't believe that I had—gone off!'

'Oh yes, he would. He said so. "Crazy white woman", is what he said.'

Gone off! The phrase rang through her head like an alarm tocsin. Gone off! A major storm was coming, and he had told the only witness that she had 'gone off'. Oh God help me, she sighed to herself, he's setting the stage. He means to do it! And he's watching me like a hawk!

'I have to change,' she babbled, sidling towards the door.

'No you don't, Teresa,' he said coldly. He caught her by the wrist and pulled her back. 'What you need to do more than anything else in all the world is to stop running, and talk to me. And we're going to do it now.'

He half dragged, half led her over to the easy chair, and plumped her into it. Then he grabbed up one of the straight chairs, turned it around so that the back faced her, and straddled it. He put his arms over the back of the chair, and rested his chin on his arms.

'There's been enough of this evasion and hiding,' he told her. 'Out on the ice I thought we were getting somewhere, but then I began to think better of it. The only reason you ever let me come near you was because you thought we were going to die. You did think that, didn't you?'

She tried to avoid his gaze, but he was close enough to turn her head back towards him with two fingers. 'Yes,' she whispered. 'Yes, I did.'

'And that was the reason you were willing to share yourself with me on the island. You thought that would be our last night, too?'

'Yes. Yes, damn you. I already told you that. Why do you have to torment me?'

'Because I want you, Teresa. I've always wanted you. I wanted you when you were a little girl, and I want the woman you've become. Why are you scared to death of me?'

'I've always—been afraid of you. I still am. Can't you leave me alone?'

He shook his head in disgust. 'No, I can't leave you alone, Teresa. You're part of me. You think a man can amputate his heart?'

'Yes. I think you can. That's what you plan to do—right now. Just the way your mother said!'

'Why do you have to keep raging about my mother? Give it a break. She's long dead and gone. And if she had sins, she's paying for them!'

'No she isn't. I'm paying for them. Leave me alone!'

He cursed, jumped up from his chair, and stalked around the room, trying to hold on to the edges of his temper. Outside the sun had disappeared, and the wind was building. He looked out towards the sea, pounded his right fist into his left palm, and walked over to the shelf where his pipe and tobacco were waiting. He brought them back with him, and sat down as before.

She watched him go through the ritual of filling his pipe and lighting it up. Her arms were stiff along the rests of the chair, her fingers almost blue from clutching at the wooden supports. He waved the smoke away, and stared at her.

'You've become the rabbit again,' he said. 'Look at your shaking. What the devil do you think I'm going to do to you?'

'I know!' she snarled at him. 'Get it over with!'

'Get it over hell!' he snarled back at her. 'First you'll tell me all about Joshua!'

The tension was too much for her. Devils were beating at her brain, shaking her shoulders. And that name on his lips was the final assault weapon. She could fight back no longer. A tiny tear formed in one corner of her eye, and she slumped down in the chair.

'Tell me about Joshua,' he repeated.

Her voice was a dejected monotone. There was no courage left in her. 'I had a baby,' she said, and waited for his reaction.

'I know that,' he said calmly, puffing at his pipe. 'Who was the father? Joshua?'

Her eyes blazing with anger, she half rose from the chair, but her rebellion lacked strength, and was shortlived. She fell back into the seat. 'You were,' she whispered. 'You were. Your mother *did* tell you, didn't she!'

He ignored the question, but there was a haunted look in those deep eyes of his. 'Tell me the rest of it,' he said softly. 'Tell me the whole story.'

'I—I wanted to tell you, that day in Houston,' she sighed. 'You wouldn't take the time to listen. When I came back to New Bedford I was two months pregnant. After the operations on my hand, I tried to work for a while, but—he was born prematurely, at seven and a half months. He had—such a wonderful child!'

'And you called him Joshua?'

'Yes. He was so tiny. I wanted him to grow big like—I—' The tears came now, quiet streams down cold cheeks.

'And where is he now?'

She looked at him with astonishment. 'Where is he?'

'For God's sake woman, you're talking about *my* son! Where is he?'

She struggled to make some sense out of what he was saying, and then she thought she understood. 'Oh,' she replied, 'I thought—I'm sorry. Yes, Papa had a place for our entire family. We put him there. In Sacred Heart cemetery.'

'In Sacred Heart—you mean he died?' His pipe had gone out, but he had not noticed.

'Of course,' she said quietly. 'You knew that. Your mother told you. He was born prematurely. There was a defect in his heart. He only lived two days. Just long enough to be baptised, and for me to hold him once in my arms. Just once. Do you know what that means, damn you!'

She flared up at him, jumping out of her chair, and pushing him and his chair back away from her. 'Look at me,' she screamed. 'I'm just built to be a mother! And I only held him once. I never ever got to feed him, to share the world with him. He was born, and then he was gone. And Papa told your mother, and she came to the hospital and laughed. Damn you! She laughed. And then she came back the next day and told me she had telephoned you, and she told me what you said—and—why do you want to torture me now, when it's six years behind me, and almost—God, how I hate you and your crazy family!'

She burst by him and ran for the door of her bedroom, slamming it behind her. Then she fell on to the bed and cried her heart out for memories. Those of long ago, and those of yesterday. There was a scent of rosemary in her tears as they dribbled over her cheek and into her mouth.

At some time after that, she slept. It was a cataleptic sleep, arms and legs straight and rigid, getting no rest, finding no release. When she woke the lamp in her room was lit, and Tim was staring down at her. Outside the window the storm had graduated from annoyance to blizzard, and she could hear the driving wind banging at the glass.

'Better?' he asked.

'Will I ever get better?' she asked stormily. 'You've come to do it, haven't you!'

'Why—yes, I guess I have,' he said. His eyebrows rose as if something that she was saying didn't make sense.

'I won't fight you,' she said woefully. 'I don't have the strength any more. Go ahead. Get it over with!'

He sat down at the side of the bed and began slowly to unbutton the front fastenings of her dress. Her eyes followed his fingers, startled. He followed the line of buttons down to the hem of her dress, and slipped her arms out, leaving her to lie there in tiny bra and briefs.

She stretched out one hand and stopped him. 'Please, Tim,' she pleaded, her eyes brimming with tears. 'For the sake of what we once were, do it quickly. Don't shame me!'

His fingers stopped in mid-air. 'What the hell, Teresa?' he exclaimed. 'What do you think I'm going to do to you?'

'I—you know,' she gasped through the tears. 'Your mother told me. She said I was to blame for Joshua's death. She said if I had been a good wife the baby would have been born whole. She said that when she told you, you got into a terrible rage, and promised her that you would come and kill me!'

'Oh my God, Teresa,' he said, appalled. 'My mother told you that? No wonder you've been running for all these years! What a bloody damn fool I've been! I don't want to kill you—I want to love you! I never ever heard a word from my mother about the baby. Not a word!'

His two hands came to rest on either side of her throat, and his thumbs were stroking the soft skin. 'You must have! You must have known!' she stammered at him. 'You knew I had a baby!'

'Why of course I did,' he said softly. 'When I put you to bed that first night out on the island, I could see the stretch marks.'

'And you knew his name was Joshua!'

'Well, I knew there was someone by the name of Joshua. I thought he was a friend of yours, maybe even the father of your baby. How could I not know. Every time you went to sleep you kept saying his name. Joshua, Joshua, Joshua! I thought I'd go mad with jealousy!'

'It's really true, Tim? You wouldn't—you wouldn't lie to me?' She managed to get control of her tears, and was able to see him clearly. She reached out one trembling hand and brushed the cowlick back from his forehead. 'All those years?' she marvelled. 'She lied to us both?'

'She might have, but I won't lie to you, Terry. All those years. All because of one crazy woman!'

'It wasn't all her fault,' she said. 'It really wasn't. I should have had the courage to call you, or to write you, or—to go and see you. I was just too afraid! Whenever I felt that you were getting close to me, I had to run!'

'I'm close now. Do you feel like running?'

'I—no, I don't. Where could I run to? Everything I ever wanted is right here. I can't believe it. I just can't believe it!'

'What can't you believe?'

'I can't believe that the fear is gone. That it's not true! Lord, my mother was right—we each make our own heaven and our own hell, and bear our devils along with us on our shoulders all our days!'

'Smart woman, your mother.'

'I thought so. Oh, Tim, how can I tell you how much I love you. What are you doing?'

'I think you have something in your eye. Besides tears, I mean.'

'That's not my eye. What are you—'

'How does this thing unfasten?'

She was giggling now, having swung from one emotional peak to another. 'It's a French one. There's a clip in the front.'

'Very practical people, the French. Now I've got it! What are you trembling for now? You're not afraid still?'

'Yes, I'm afraid. I'm afraid you'll stop. I'm not trembling. It's just that there's so much of me—when I breathe deep—ahhhhhhhh.'

'Jelly never tasted this good. You taste good, Teresa. Want me to stop?'

'I'll kill you if you do! I—oh God, Tim, hurry! It's been so long!'

Late that night—very late, she stirred one eye open and looked around. Two inches in front of her nose was his, his breath coming heavily after the storm of passion, eyes squeezed tight, fast asleep. She trailed one finger across his forehead, through the straggling straw of his soft hair. They were both lying, nude, on top of the sheets, and the wind was whirling up a major storm outside. Carefully she hitched her way out of his arms and off the bed. It was a struggle to move the blankets from under him, but she succeeded. She covered him over, blew out the lamp, and climbed back into bed. He grunted as she snuggled up to him, and one of his arms dropped to her waist, the hand clutching at the curve of her hip.

She held her breath, hoping first not to disturb him, and then later, when she had regained her senses, hoping that she *would* disturb him. But the day had been too long—and the night also! She chuckled, and he slept on. And so did she when the warmth and comfort enveloped her. For the first time in years she slept well and long, without nightmares, but not exactly without dreams.

When she woke up, it was almost afternoon. Her watch marked the eleventh hour, but the whirling demons of the arctic storm had obliterated any chance for sunlight.

'Tim,' she called. His head popped around the door as if he had been standing guard. 'Then it wasn't a dream?' she asked.

'No, it wasn't a dream, Mrs Alden,' he replied. 'One cup of coffee coming up. No toast. There isn't any bread. Care for a chunk of jerky?'

'No, you fool,' she laughed. She snatched a pillow from behind her head and threw it in the general direction of the door.

'Well, you don't have to abuse me,' he said dolefully. 'I'm an old family retainer, you know.

'Emphasis on the *old*?' she enquired archly. 'The party was over pretty early last night!'

'Hey, I'm just an average guy, not a satyr.'

'There's nothing average about you, Tim Alden,' she said. 'You saved my life. What average engineer goes running out into the path of a polar bear, shouting advertising jingles? What average man knows how to take a scared girl on an ice trek?'

'Now that you mention it, I take that back,' he laughed. 'I don't know any man who couldn't do with a little judicious hero-worship! About forty years'-worth?'

'Perhaps. Although I suspect that by the time I get to be seventy I won't be able to bend over to kiss your foot. You did say coffee?'

'Okay, okay,' he grumbled, backing out the door. 'How soon they forget!'

He came back in ten minutes, with two steaming cups of coffee, and a bowl of canned peaches. 'The darn fire almost went out,' he explained. 'Somebody forgot to put coal on the fire last night!'

'And somebody,' she chuckled, 'has got to trudge over to the other building and put coal in that boiler.'

'Ah. You like the peaches?' he asked, stealing one from her spoon, and then kissing the juice off her lips. 'Now, about that boiler. I think since we're an intrepid exploring team, and this is the year of Woman's Liberation, that we ought to cut cards and establish a duty roster?'

'Drink your coffee and dream on,' she told him saucily. 'I'm an officer in the United States Air Force. Officers don't shovel coal into boilers!'

'They don't? What do they do?' They had finished the coffee and the peaches, and he was stretched out beside her on the bed, he on the outside, dressed, she underneath, naked.

'Well, I'm not sure I can tell you,' she said, pursing her lips. 'You remember what they used to say about the settlers on Cape Cod?'

'No. What?'

'They used to say that in the summer they fished and made babies, and in the wintertime they couldn't do much fishing!'

'Are you trying to tell me something?'

'Yes. Can't you decode the message? I thought all MIT graduates were great scholars.'

'You've got that just a smidgin wrong. All MIT students are great scholars. After we graduate we find out how dumb we are!'

'Tim,' she said solemnly. 'We are married, aren't we?'

'Yes, of course. Don't bother me, I'm thinking.'

'Me too. Tim, do you think that we could—that you wouldn't mind if we— were to have another baby?' The last words of the sentence spurted out at double speed, and she sat up to search his face. 'Tim?'

'I have to think that over,' he said. 'We've got a bigger problem than that facing us.'

'Bigger than a baby? How could that be?'

'Our problem is as big as the United States Air Force, girl. You're a member of the military service. Have you forgotten? I'm a civilian. Suppose they order you to Timbucktoo, or something? And I refuse to sleep at attention, either! No, what we have to do is to get you out of the military service.'

'Man, that's patriotism for you. We don't need the money?'

'No, we don't need the money, you goon. Stop talking and start thinking.'

'How can I think when you keep running your hand over my—stop it, Tim. I'm thinking. I'm thinking!'

'It's about time. I'm going for another cup of coffee.' He struggled up from the bed and walked out. When he came back, balancing two mugs filled to the brim, her eyes were bright with devils, and there was a very large smile on her face. He said two four-letter words as the hot coffee slopped over on to his hand.

'I have thought of an idea,' she told him, her whole face lit up.

'So tell me before I burn myself to death,' he said.

'Well—' she hesitated. 'How soon do you have to make the next radio check?'

'Twelve days. What's the idea?'

'Twelve days. Well—maybe it would work.'

'Don't diddle! What's the idea?'

'According the Air Force Regulations, a female officer who enters into the reproductive cycle from legitimate causes, may submit her resignation without prejudice under Chapter XIX. That's what.'

'Let me have that again in small print?'

'Pregnant officers can quit!'

'Well, hell,' he laughed, 'that solves our problem!' He put the two cups of coffee down on the bedside table, and danced a little jig. 'Come on, girl,' he called to her, 'we'll have a dance to celebrate.'

'The devil we will,' she told him. 'In two weeks' time the rescue team will be here. There's hardly enough time as it is. Come to bed, Tim, and let's get started on my resignation!'

Harlequin Intrigue®

Trust No One...

When you are outwitting a cunning killer, confronting dark secrets or unmasking a devious imposter, it's hard to know whom to trust. Strong arms reach out to embrace you—but are they a safe harbor...or a tiger's den?

When you're on the run, do you dare to fall in love?

For heart-stopping suspense and heart-stirring romance, read Harlequin Intrigue. Two new titles each month.

HARLEQUIN INTRIGUE—where you can expect the unexpected.

What a great Ice Lady in Greenland! Teresa was full of adventure + good luck with your BABY.

HARLEQUIN

Romance

**This October,
travel to England with
Harlequin Romance
FIRST CLASS title #3155
TRAPPED
by Margaret Mayo**

"I'm my own boss now and I intend to stay that way."

Candra Drake loved her life of freedom on her narrow-boat
home and was determined to pursue her career as a company
secretary free from the influence of any domineering man.
Then enigmatic, arrogant Simeon Sterne breezed into her life,
forcing her to move and threatening a complete takeover of her
territory and her heart....